EDITORS Roxane Gay, M. Bartley Seigel **ASSOCIATE EDITORS** Brad Green, Sheila Squillante **READERS** Matthew Burnside, Joshua Diamond, Jaime Fountaine, T.J. Jarrett, Jen Knox, Derrick Martin-Campbell, Joe Stracci, Robb Todd, Matthew Robinson, Luke Thominet, Patrick Trotti **COPY EDITOR** Lynn Crothers **INTERNS** Alyssa Friske, Kurt Benson **ADVISORY BOARD** Cecil Giscombe, Bob Hicok, Taylor Mali, Michael Martone, Daniel Nester, Amber Tamblyn, Keith Taylor, Kette Thomas, Deb Olin Unferth **DESIGN** Alban Fischer **COVER ART** Rachel Frank, (l-r) "Hill Rd.", "Untitled", "Marlee", and "Untitled"; inside title: "Michael". ✳ ✳ ✳ Founded in 2006, the nonprofit literary arts collective PANK—*PANK* Magazine, pankmagazine.com, the Little Book Series, and the Invasion Readings—fosters access to emerging and experimental poetry and prose, publishing the brightest and most promising writers for the most adventurous readers. To the end of the road, up country, a far shore, the edge of things, to a place of amalgamation and unplumbed depths, where the known is made and unmade, and where unimagined futures are born, a place inhabited by contradictions, a place of quirk and startling anomaly, PANK, no soft pink hands allowed. Direct all correspondence to PANK, 305 Walker Center, 1400 Townsend Dr., Houghton, Michigan 49931, or email awesome@pankmagazine.com. Online issues, subscription and donation information, and submission guidelines are available at www.pankmagazine.com. Any resemblance to actual events, locales, or persons, living or dead, in creative works contained herein is entirely coincidental. Opinions and views contained herein are not necessarily those of the editors. ISSN: 1935-7133. Copyright © 2013 PANK.

SONG OF MY BEDROOM SKIN

ALEXIS POPE

y bones break without touching anything. I walk up the stairs to my apartment and fracture each toe. I'm not sure how I heal. Remember the dark on flesh where my legs used to be? There was an absence of feeling, which is average.

There was a large glass of milk on the table. There was a bubble to fill in but I didn't. I never follow directions and maybe that's why he found me. In the corner of the market, I stole berries & ate them in the public bathroom. I took a nap on the floor & woke to the sound of knocking. A middle-aged woman expressed her frustrations with a container of orange juice. My barcode was expired & I followed him downstairs. On the basement floor I left my head while he fucked me. I ate the light from his mouth. Fatigued his weight against my other parts, the parts that milk with shattered anger. I turned into a moth before he finished.

When I circled my hand around him, I already knew what to expect. Each excitement punished with routine. My wrongness turned on & I stole the rhubarb. I stuck it down my pants & it lived there until I arrived home. I broke nine toes that time.

In my room, I imagined sitting on him. Different settings with my hand in my most familiar dark. I sat on him in the passenger seat. I sat on him on the bar stool & crowded the exit sign with my want down his jeans. I fucked him at the bus stop. He ate me with my back against the sidewalk. He babysat my ache, let me cry for three hours after. I filled the shopping cart with eggplant. I filled a minute with soft moans. I filled him with my deep ocean. I couldn't get off because I was too sad. The street lamp entered my bedroom & I fucked it. It burnt out like most things. He told me I tasted like lemons.

I drove to the mall to remind myself that I'm going to die. I broke my arm when the woman at the beauty kiosk tried to lotion my hands. She was frightened. I tried to not think about his warm, his muscle eyes, his hard center where I buried myself most nights.

I brushed my hair in the bedroom and dislocated my shoulder. Apples fell from inside. They hit the floor with a familiar thump. I closed my eyes and could still feel my head against the wall. I was a meal last night. I felt like a rain onto him. My water mirrors his face

& I want to drink all of it. I gulp down his soft hands. I race back into the store basement to hold myself and say his name in between breaths. I am my most fucked self when he lives in my brain. I want to swallow everything. When he cried I felt like dying.

I told him I wanted to hold all of it for him. He kissed me and I knew what that meant. Sometimes my body is the whole answer. I fell onto the floor and broke myself the only way I could.

M.E. IN TROUBLE

ALICE BRADLEY

M.E. told me this story and he swore it was true, nothing but true, and made me hope to die I wouldn't tell anyone but God. We were hiding on his roof after Joseph P. said he would beat my brains in, after M.E. beat on him and Joseph P. fell down and we made a run for it. Anyone driving by M.E.'s house could look up and see two boys all bruised and torn jeans, lying there, too tired to do much except wait for his dad to find us. We stared at the sky until I thought we might fall into space, and I lifted my less-painful hand and swore. He said "That was too easy for a liar like you" but he told me anyway.

M.E. was in his pajamas, setting up his racing cars in his room when the noise downstairs died down to nothing. He looked up and heard what wasn't there: no dad slamming doors, no stepmother going at his sister Lucky, no sister Lucky outside his window yelling numbers with each jump-rope slap. M.E. dropped his cars and leaned over to see into Lucky's room: it was a wide-open mouth, no bed, no rug, only thumbtacks and white shapes on the walls where posters should be. The quiet filled the room and his lungs, the quiet pushed him straight out, and in the hallway the windows shook like tissues and the walls breathed, go, go, and he did. M.E. skidded around the banister and three jumps down the stairs out the front door in time to see his dad and stepmother shoving suitcases into the station wagon. He yelled from the porch, what? where?, but his dad kept on rearranging suitcases and even furniture, all disappearing into the back of the car. M.E.'s stepmother looked at her watch and then at the sky. M.E.'s sister Lucky stood by the open door of the station wagon with her Barbie, and bounced its Barbie feet across the car. M.E. wished someone had told him earlier they were leaving so he wouldn't have set up his cars. He stood on the cold steps in his bare feet, and his father and stepmother turned and put up a hand each and their mouths shouted nothing.

M.E. could see their mouths open but couldn't hear because of the noise, a snapping noise like when he went swimming and he had to smack his head until his ear popped. He yelled back but they kept waving, waving him away, keeping him on the porch. His stepmother took Lucky by the arm and pushed her into the back seat. Lucky spread out and smiled at M.E. and shook her Barbie at him—all the back seat to herself, no brother poking at her! Then everyone was in the car, and his stepmother's hair flew out the open window like small hands waving as the car went backward into the street and down the street and away.

In M.E.'s house the lights were blazing and the curtains tied shut. The TV was on so loud he thought maybe it was a party. A surprise, all for him. Instead a man with a huge face stared out at the TV room and above the drowning water noises the TV man laughed. In the kitchen he heard a bang and M.E. ran in to catch someone. But there was no one, only the empty cabinets knocked open and the refrigerator buzzing. The top of the stove lit up with flames, FOOMP. M.E. jumped and shouted Motherfuck! and when no one yelled about the language he shouted it again and again, and that is when he saw the eye.

It was down the hall when M.E. saw it, in a mirror over the company-only couch. In the mirror it looked like a drawing of an eye, like a balloon with an eye painted on it—but then the eye closed and opened. Its stick lashes slapped down and rolled back, and it slid past the mirror and was gone. The stove lit up high again, FOOMP, and M.E. went straight for the stairs. He heard something brush against the wall behind him, a dry raspy thing, and he shouted the best curses he knew and tore upstairs and into his room. He slammed the door and locked it and remembered how the door doesn't lock anymore ever since his dad punched it open. All he could think was to hide under the bed, but he could only half-fit. He laid under there with his legs and feet out in the room shaking and he listened to it slide and screech against the banister. It scratched at his door and at least, he thought, when it got him he wouldn't have to see it. He heard the door open and

something dry and cold settled on his foot while its breath whistled in and out and he was so scared, M.E. says, that he fell asleep.

M.E. woke up in the morning in the same spot with his still-shut-hard head aching. A cold hand clamped down his foot and pulled and he yelled. "Try sleeping on the bed for once," his stepmother said. Then she was out the door, shouting, "I'm not making breakfast all day so get down here." M.E. had a slow, careful look around the bedrooms, the dresser drawers filled and Lucky's stupid posters all over. And downstairs was Lucky at the table and his dad in the yard smoking a cigarette. He waited for his stepmother to say "Sorry about leaving you with a monster last night," but she only stood over the stove and cursed at the burned butter and Lucky sang "You're a Grand Old Flag" until M.E. told her to shut it.

The worst part, M.E. told me, is that he saw it. Even with his eyes shut, he knew. It went straight into his head because it wanted M.E. to see how scary it was for the next time. And up on his roof, he drew it in the air, his shaky finger looping its balloon head, open mouth, eyes rolling; he drew its dead arms and sick floating legs, and I wish he hadn't.

M.E. has a plan. He's waiting for the next time it comes and his family leaves him. Next time he's not going to run and hide his head. M.E.'s going to call me as soon as his parents get near the car with their suitcases; if it's not me who picks up he will hit the buttons on the phone and that way I'll know. If someone at my house says, "Why are you pressing buttons and not speaking?" I'll know it's M.E. and I will run over with my knife. Because, M.E. says, it doesn't think there are going to be two boys, and not two boys with a knife, and especially not two boys with a great knife like I have. And when his family creeps in early the next morning with their suitcases, whispering, is it done? we'll be there with the thing dead at our feet, and his parents will be so ashamed they'll leave us alone to live there, nothing will come at us again and if it does, I have my knife.

I keep my knife with me, so when the call comes I don't waste time. If the phone rings and my brother says, "Hello?" and hangs up, I ask what did he hear—but he always says nothing. And then he says, "You got a date with your girlfriend M.E.?" and wheezes his hyena laugh until I throw a couch pillow at him and he jumps me. My brother thinks M.E. makes up stories, not this one because I didn't tell, but other stories M.E. has told.

My brother doesn't understand that "story" doesn't mean "not true." It's like how I tell my teachers my mom is dead, when actually she moved to Florida and we don't know her number. Or that time I found a head on the beach, rolled in seaweed, the blue rotting head of a man. I told M.E., I told my teacher and my grandmother, and I told the policeman who walked me across the beach. We slipped on the wet rocks and the foam and the policeman kept saying how lying was dangerous. It was here, I told him, it was here. I got a long stick and knocked over rocks and stopped to dig, to show him I meant it, it was here. He was telling me like I didn't know, like I couldn't say what was real and what was not, but he didn't know what was real; he couldn't say until he saw.

It was getting darker and the tide coming in; the policeman put his hand on my neck which made me jump and I shouted and he said stop. We were right there before the big rocks, where the seaweed covers everything so you can barely walk from sliding. And there in a chain of seaweed ringing the water, there was something humped over, black-knotted and shining. I said here, I got my stick, I poked it, here, and it rolled over, here. The policeman shouted, grabbed at me, pulled my face into his chest and he said don't look, and he thought I was crying but I was laughing, because I said it was true and it was true and he saw it was true, and I held on to him while the tide and everything roared.

GEFFREY DAVIS VENISON

In my previous life as a deer, I honed my brand
of nervousness, balanced instinct and memory,
sharpened that ability to slip silently between
thicket and meadow, changing from fluid motion
to some frozen effigy of the thing—: existence
reduced to traveling my predispositions. Poised
over the hard hoof, I tested the live weight of
never feeling all the way prepared, searched out
spoiled apples beneath winter's ice, at a moment
ready to morph into a fleeing patch of white
haunch among the naked trees. I raced against
the hunter's success, against the day
he would strike the muskiness of my hide
and the hot, mercurial life beneath it—: carve me,
freeze me, the velvet vastness of my body
parceled out to loved ones, in easily stored pieces.

GEFFREY DAVIS

WHAT I MEAN
WHEN I SAY FOREVER

This messy mathematics of memory, this overlooking of remainders—
we divide our loved ones from the interplay of seasons. What remainders

we recount we'll spread like petals at their feet. Later, I may even add
a little bit of wind to the ordinariness of this day, if only so she'll remain

as taut with life as she is now, dancing on the lawn between cigarettes,
the threat of subtraction pressed between her lips. *Stay,* I plead, *remain—*

promise not to die. And she does, she vows the impossible multiplication
of her breaths, swears to spend her widowed years splayed like a remainder

caught in the taciturn equation of tomorrow. She gives me her hand 36.5
thousand more times. *Good laps around the sun,* she would say, *still remain*

for us. And we go on like this, forgetting the formulas of our existence.
We make unions from this failure to weigh what may not remain.

THIS BITTER PILL

FRANK BILL

Heroin, sometimes called Dope, H, Mud, Smack, Mexican Horse, Hell Dust, and Junk is a highly addictive and rapidly acting opiate. Heroin is produced from morphine, a principal component of opium, a natural occurring substance that is extracted from the seedpod of the opium poppy. It's color ranges from a white or brown powder, to a solid black substance that is sometimes sticky and referred to as black tar. As of 2003, nearly 3,091,000 US residents aged 12 and older have used heroin at least once in their lifetime.

—**National Drug Intelligence Center**

Cleaving the pockets of her denim, Tar Baby needs more than the lint that lines the cotton to pay back a debt to the heroin pipeline of Harrison County, a liability that satisfied the screams reaming her and her boyfriend's insides so they could swim in the feeling of heated foam last week.

She stands behind the counter of the English Mini-Mart, jagged and tactile, her arms scarred like graffiti on bathroom stalls, watching the 78 Thunderbird with a Bit-O-Honey-colored top pull up to one of two gas pumps through the smeared glass. From it steps a man linked with cellophane muscle beneath a sleeveless V-neck, his pants hang half off his ass, the stitch of boxers rimming his lower back.

The bell above the door jingles and the obligation of her addiction weighs heavy on her eighteen-year-old conscience. Deuce bows his head to get through the opening, he's tatted with the numeral two about his neck and shoulders in the font of Roman, Franklin Gothic and Courier. His teeth glow white, some bordered with gold, and his serpentine eyes cut into Tar Baby.

The low croon of coolers that wall the left side of the shoebox-store where colas, teas, juices and sports drinks are refrigerated is the only sound heard. She stares into some thought he cannot see but fathoms all too well, one where she dissolves the cumin-colored powder in liquid, heats it in a spoon, ties off an appendage, flicks and breaks her pigment with a needle.

Deuce tells her, "You and yur boyfriend, Patch Work, got credit that need recompensated."

Weeks ago, after birthing their baby boy, Ezekiel, into the world, the new wore off and that yearn to have their cavities waxed came calling. Tar Baby and Patch Boy went slumming, got their eyes rolled into their skulls and drool down their chins til the cash given by relatives for the newborn dried up. They'd bought enough **H** from Deuce to get it fronted, thinking her pay from the mart and Patch's scrap money would settle up the barter, and it would have if they'd not bought formula, diapers, some Oxy and Patch's truck hadn't broken down. Now, every nerve ending in Tar Baby's frame shrieked with the fright of owing this man while craving what he pushed.

"We gonna pay." She says.

"Don't be playin' me fo some dumb shit redneck."

Her shoulders and knees belt, as she imagines a tiny rivulet of blood expanding around the dissolve of the rig, the **Hell Dust** sizzling inside her like heated grease, frying the endorphins, dropping her back to a state of the perished.

"We ain't playin' you. Money been tight with us raisin' a newborn. Livin' at Patch's mama and stepdaddy's trailer."

Her tongue ovals her lips, she wants to feel her vanilla tissue beneath her nails. Deuce leans down, still taller than her and rests his forearms on the counter, "One of you's gonna pay me notes or" he pauses and reaches a sharpie digit toward her chin, runs it over her ear and finishes with, "by skin."

Smelling Deuce's saltine cracker and ashtray-stubbed body sickens her. Deuce bends back to standing and her whites are sunken lines of mascara that meet the fist of his crotch, she knows how he doesn't treat females, he cuffs them, mars them and strobes them with shanks and syringes for days on end in the back bedroom of his trailer. She's heard testaments to the horror he calls payment.

Deuce sucks on the enamel of his teeth, takes in the shapes beneath her Rob Zombie concert T-shirt, looks to a door by the coolers, behind it is the storage room and he says, "Maybe I make you *lay down* what you owe now."

She sees it in his face, him imaging her bent over the boxes of canned goods or potato chips and a chord of terror gauges her like a razor and she says, "No, Patch and me get whut we owe you."

"When?" he demands, slamming his hand on the register.

"Tomorrow." She lies.

Before she can blink Deuce's palm fills her vision. Meshes her lower lip again the marrow rooted in her gums. The taste of ore warms her taste buds and he tells her, "They's more of that you and yo boy don't pay up."

Tar Baby stutter steps into the wall behind her, wrist dabbing at her mouth, she watches Deuce reach for a carton of Newports that are stacked above where she stood.

"I take these and some gas, call it interest on what I front you two junkies."

Tracking over the floor, he pauses and says, "Be back tomorrow for my coin or yo husk." Then exits out the glass framed by scuffed steel and Tar Baby dams her sight, battles the impulse to scream at Deuce to stop, take her into the back, use her til she and Patch Boy are no longer indebted and maybe even a little extra if he'll give her some **Mud** to silence her ache.

✳

Before the barnacled truck door slams, Elmer shakes his head and tells Tar Baby, "Won't be stoppin' to give you a lift no more." Then the truck goes left at the T and she walks the opposite direction along the right flank of the road.

Every evening since Patch Boy's truck broke down this has been her getting back and forth to work. Elmer not driving the extra mile to the trailer. But stopping, offering her a ride on his way home from the chicken plant when he sees her, he flirts with her and preaches his words of scripture.

Elmer's got bloodhound cheeks, flecks of tobacco in his teeth and smells of spoiled fowl. "God got a plan for us all, you'll see." He told her this evening after questioning the swell of her lip and she told him she'd hit it on a cooler door at the mart.

And Tar Baby fights her body's pleas for a fix and says, "How you reckon the savior tastes?"

"How he tastes? Girl, what serpent has infested your tongue?"

"None," she says, "but the way you speak of him shapin' lands, formin' oceans, turning water to wine, even a grain of him would appease one's needs. I bet some'd pay top dollar."

"Girl, you has got to kick that sin-talk to a sinkhole, cover it over with answers from the good book."

All she could do was push her bony knee closer to the curious calluses of his hand that patted it in-between his spiritual oration. She wanted to ask does the Lord's plan involve fifty-year-old men and eighteen-year-old girls who cannot pay a heroin-peddling sadist except with her hide. Desperate she asked Elmer, "How much would you pay to get down my pants, for me to spill your gravy?"

And like that her transit from the mart had ended. Now she'd have to do as she did in the mornings, thumb a ride to work from the vehicles in the holler that zoomed past with the rusted squeak of axles and the cough of exhaust soot.

✳

The dented tin trailer with a red stripe that's been bleached to pink by the sun, sits with a couch the color of a coyote's hide in the dirt yard by two pine trees. A Chevy S10 with a blown head gasket sits parked with rungs of copper wire, an aluminum screen door and a stovetop in the bed. Tar Baby takes the steps up the warped deck, turns the doorknob that's actually a screwdriver handle, smelling chemical smoke and hearing Ezekiel crying over the thump of rustic Americana music before the door is opened.

Inside, the room has been mugged of all that is good, replaced by every shade of what's wrong with Tar Baby's world. Of wants and needs that shouldn't be. Things others pretend no longer exist. But this bitter pill called the truth of un-salvaged lives does endure.

Patch Boy's stepfather sits like a Crisco stain on the kitchen counter, oily and slick. He's shirtless, his ribs poke out like elongated fingers, he sometimes touches her, calls her his daughter-in-law, but she reads his affection, his accidently walking in when she's toweling the beads from her stretch marked breasts, hips and stomach after showering. His saying 'I sorry' but still smiling with teeth that are broken shards of lactose dipped in Hersey syrup, taking in a final glimpse of her shapes before closing the bathroom door.

In the kitchen sits Patch Boy, he's still-brained and stutters but scores good drugs. He cries some nights about his real father, a man who loved him wrong, gave him the same love his father, Patch's grandfather, gave him.

The mother sits across from Patch Boy, not paying any mind to Tar Baby, passing a clear pipe that's the size of a baseball to the son. He presses it to his lips. Fires a lighter, the resin pot bubbles with water as he huffs the smoke.

The mother's robust with fish-batter curls and an eyeshot of pink glaze. She exhales toxins and says, "Bout time you got home. Can change that damn squealer of yours. Been barkin' fur near an hour."

Tar Baby wants some of what they're sharing, something to seer this edge off of what must be paid to Deuce but Ezekiel's crying beckons her. The stereo blares with Ray Wylie Hubbard's tune *Opium* as the stepfather stomps the floor and slaps his knee. She speaks over all of this to Patch. "He come by the mart today."

Patch turns to her with a scalp nicked by shears, knuckles and barbed wire, he blinks and stammers, "Who..who..who come—" and he stops short, noticing Tar Baby's puffed lip.

"Deuce." She says.

A tear forms within Patch Boy's vision and he says, "He..he..he be touchin' you."

She thought of Deuce's finger rounding her ear, his eyeing her chest, the carton of smokes he took and the gas.

"He want his coin for the **Junk**."

"We..we… dddon't… got it."

"Deuce gonna be payin' another visit to the mart tomorrow."

"You..you..don't wwwork tomorrow."

"I know, buyin' us some space." She hesitates and tells Patch Boy, "He say I can pay with myself."

"He bbbest st..st..step back."

The stepfather barks, "Ain't no sable be beddin' my boy's female less he wanna a mouth full of gunpowder and pellets."

Patch Boy scratches the stub of his crown, dandruff flakes and falls to his shoulders and he asks, "When..when you..you get yur check?"

"Friday."

"Th..then he..he gonna have tttuh wait."

The stepfather grazes Tar Baby's neck.

She wants to smoke her lungs or roast her inner wadding. She spins, swats the stepfather's wormy clasp, and demands, "Whut about you?"

His façade pinches and draws and he says, "Whut about me?"

"Tender, you got any we can barrow?"

"Got none til Friday. Me and the queen tossed our last dime on a eight ball of crankshaft-candy."

Tar Baby mumbles, "That do us no damn good," and brushes past him.

"Hold on a damn minute girl. You's family and family caters to its own." The stepfather says as he watches her walk down the hallway to the squall of her child.

Ezekiel's heaves churn off the panel board walls, grabbing him from the crate where he lays in unrest, he is warm but not from body temperature, it's from his tainted diaper that has leaked onto his Tigger and Pooh blanket. Laying him on a dresser to be changed, his face wrinkles, she rips the sides of the diaper, his hands crimp to his mouth, tiny fingers the size of bloated maggots curl, his eyes wide and ocean blue, she wads the heft into a lump. Reaches for a baby wipe, cleans the smears from his bottom, clasps a fresh absorbent around him. And Deuce's offer hangs over her like another layer of skin.

*

One morning passes as her day off, when the next comes she sits on the rotted and mildewed front porch, a blanket burrowed around her, a cigarette between her crusty lips watching the sun lift over a mess of cedar across the road. It is a Wednesday and a cordless phone rests next to a line of empty Miller High Life bottles on the deck's railing, smoke pipes from her mouth. She has phoned Mr. Alcorn, the owner of the mart, tells him she's not feeling well. Mr. Alcorn questions her about fuel and a carton of smokes, nearly seventy dollars of combined sales that were inventoried on Tuesday but unaccounted for. Tar Baby has no answers and the owner tells her she is fired. Tar Baby does not argue, says, "I be in on Friday to get my check." The owner tells her, "The gas and cigarettes will be deducted from yur pay."

Gravel crimps beneath rubber as a maroon Lincoln stops in the driveway, the thump of base rattles the trunk, then goes deaf with the engine. The driver's side opens and a wheel barrel of weight plants his feet on the ground, his complexion is a face of infected pores and a chaff of hair that appears singed and mangled.

Tar Baby knows not who this man is but why he has come. Behind her, there is the punch of feet and the trailer rocks, voices are drowned out until the door whistles open. From it the stepfather and Patch Boy step, they're bugging from two pots of coffee and a few lines of amphetamine. One holds a .22 revolver the other a dated .12 gauge pump. "You lost?" the stepfather yells.

The car's passenger side unlatches, out steps another man who appears hard as an oak fence post with a crooked ball cap and spurred lips, he points over the door at Tar Baby. "She know why we here. Settle her and Patch Boy debt to Deuce."

Tar Baby takes a final drawl from her Camel Wide, flicks it out into the dewy yard and hears the faint beginnings of Ezekiel's wailing.

Patch Boy moves past Tar Baby and trains the .22 on the one man. "Sh..sh..she ain't go..go..goin' nnnooo..where's. Deuce get his when he ggget it."

Each of the men reach and raise 9mm Glocks. The driver aims his at the stepfather, the passenger points his at Patch and says, "Yo Porky the Pig speakin' ass best put that p-shoota' down."

Tar Baby comes from sitting, her hand of chipped nail polish quakes as she pushes the barrel of the .22 toward their feet and says, "I am goin'. Deuce got tuh be paid. Go in yonder, Ezekiel needs changed and fed."

She'd phoned Deuce before Mr. Alcorn, after thinking about her life. About the gummy buds she started rolling at age fifteen, the man-made crank that she snorted at sixteen and the **Smack** she began bruising her veins with at seventeen, then became broken-knee'd and went to rehab, stayed clean until birthing Ezekiel, moved out of her parent's home and in with Patch Boy.

She does not want her child to see this life that she cannot grasp. One that never holds enough money to afford anything more than struggle and privation. She has inventoried this knowledge and takes the creaking deck boards one bare foot at a time to the yard. Walks to the car, glances back at Patch Boy who grapples for syllables to sound off the word NO.

Tar Baby screeches across the backseat, smelling the sweat-splotched vinyl and soured beer cans that are crunched about the floor. The two men get in, close the doors and the car fires to life, rhythms rime from speakers and shake her bones. She sits remembering what an addict once told her after seeing the track marks on her arms, that even after the swells of puss heal and scab, the pang of want never subsides. It's there tucked away like the blood kin that embarrasses one with a wondering orb and split-speech and is closet hid 'til the day you die.

CAROLINE CREW

DARLING EVENT HORIZON

I don't mind
being a black hole

to be this size
with the mass of a mountain

might make one consider asking
small questions of this system

instead I am sticking
to my side of the universe

because I am not ready
to talk about beauty

like the way this morning
I remembered tiny canvasses

are your whole body
and I can make them anything

Léon Bakst's *Supper*
Rothko's *Four Darks in Red*

a field guide to catastrophe

the bathroom graffiti *Sherlock, I believe*

weight is the force

of a gravity field to give life

there are several things in my body

least of all the cold remnants of stars

though light cannot escape

the collapse of the moment

CURIOUS THINGS THAT HAPPENED TO HER IN PARIS

SAM GRIEVE

THE ELEPHANT WRITER

When she is twenty one, she moves into a flat on the Boulevard Saint-Germain. It is a scruffy, capacious flat that she shares with some girls. From the drawing room window Notre Dame rises like an exquisite dream.

The other girls fight. They slam doors and call each other obscene names and puff their lips in their French way. When it gets too much she lies on her bed with a novel, her teacup balancing on a tower of book. Her room is quiet and, in the afternoon, the summer sunlight falls in a perfect rectangle on the rug. At night, however, she is sometimes woken up by a typewriter, through the wall. The old-fashioned kind, with its clickety-click keys and the buoyant *ka-ching* of the carriage return.

Eventually, she asks her flatmates about it. They have no idea what she is talking about. The apartment next door is empty, they tell her, and, in, fact the room right next to hers has been sealed off.

"It is where de Brunhoff wrote *Babar the Elephant*," Daphne tells her. "And drew the pictures. When he died they closed up the room. There is no way in now. You must have been dreaming."

But she knows what she heard. Each night she presses her water glass against the plaster of the wall and waits for him—her ghostwriter. On occasion, she hears him moving around, his tubercular cough, the squeaky adjustment of his chair, but usually he is working.

She closes her eyes and tries to picture the Sahara at night under a sickle moon. The way he might imagine it. Bleached waves of sand stretching to the horizon. The rippling shadows of dunes. A star-spattered sky.

One afternoon at a bouquiniste, she finds his biography. On the verso of the frontispiece is a portrait, which she spends a long time examining—his handsome face, the neat sweep of his hair. He was thirty seven when he died. A father. Just thinking about it makes her throat ache. In bed that night she turns on her side and faces him, lays her palm flat against the wall. She wonders what he is working on. Did they leave it all in intact for him when they closed up the room? His pens, his pencils, his brushes, stiff and dry now?

Through the wall he coughs, long and loud. She shuts her eyes.

THE DINNER PARTY

Soon after arriving, she is invited to a dinner party. The hostess is an American, the blue-blooded sort, fair, fragile, who brings a Burberry umbrella to Europe and always walks arm in arm with an ancestor, in this case an early governor of Massachusetts. The address on the invitation is Avenue Foch. It is a very prestigious address, she knows, but with a name she finds quite amusing; being, of course, alliterative of a Germanic sex act.

The dinner party consists of the hostess, a French count, a Bavarian baroness, a baron with wicked, green eyes, another French aristocrat (title lost), the son of a French politician, a couple of ordinaries, and herself. As she spoons her soup, she thinks of her own lineage, those dour farmers cracking the Scottish soil with ploughs, the solicitors, the surgeons, the runaways, the artists. The count to her left is a droning bore, and so for the first hour she keeps stealing glances at the gilt mantel clock. But as the evening progresses, things pick up. The debauched European underbelly, so well-chronicled by Henry James, is exposed through the fluff. The baron admits he is impoverished, and was recently arrested for smuggling drugs (class B). The baroness keeps filling her own wine glass. The non-titled aristocrat insults the count by calling his title

Napoleonic, which everyone understands to mean, New. Nasty words are exchanged, but luckily the politician's son chooses that moment to divulge that his mother is a famous pornographic actress. The men's interest is redirected. Her body of work is discussed at length.

Their hostesss, whose puritan soul finds this all very distressing, becomes more and more particular about form. Each course is announced, which causes a break in the flow of the wine. Even the cheese is introduced by name. The count, who has done his research on the American's family (and fortune), declines to correct her pronunciation; the cheese therefore possesses a strangely mangled flavor, more Vermont cheddar than Saint-Nectaire.

At one point the baroness tumbles right out of her chair, and the leg snaps off.

"What an old piece of Scheiße," the Baroness declares, picking herself up from the floor. Their hostess, who has been lent the apartment by a New York Somebody, disappears for a while, presumably to cry. Not a person in the room is older than twenty five.

One morning she goes to Shakespeare and Company. She has read so much about the shop but, as she approaches and spots the sunflower-yellow awning, she feels a sudden contraction of her skin. It is a trick she possesses, this making herself less visible, but she hates herself for doing it too.

The shop reeks of cats, and every book she picks up is slightly gummy under her hands or yellowed by the sun. She explores everything in utter silence: the secret corners, the battered chairs, the books piled up in heaps. At the back of the shop, behind a floral curtain, she spies a mattress tucked into a tiny alcove in the wall. A guy's Swarthmore college sweatshirt is draped over it, a notebook and pen lie to the side. She had heard about this, how young writers could stay here in exchange for some work. She is overcome with awe.

She wants to buy something, so she chooses a book by Elizabeth Bishop. As she goes up to the cash register, she realizes that the old man perched behind the desk is George Whitman himself, friend to Sylvia Beach. Her hand trembles as she hands over her money, but Whitman does not notice; he is preoccupied with a scruffy American (the writer, she surmises) who is talking loudly about his work. Would George let him do a reading?

George forgets to give her change, so she takes her book and heads out. The writer is still talking. He smells rather unwashed.

On her way home she passes the Café de Cluny, and for the hell of it, she sits at a table and orders a drink Hemingway drank a lot of in *A Moveable Feast, a fine*. The waiter is startled by her request but brings it to her nonetheless. The drunk at the bar winks at her with a rheumy eye. She stares out at the square, at the fountain, the pigeons, the clusters of tourists with their cameras. She cannot stop thinking about that writer's bed, about his loud, sure voice. She is overcome with disillusion. It is like a world she can peer into, but it is also a world in which she feels like an intruder—no, worse, an imposter. She would never have the confidence to speak to Whitman, let alone request accommodation; although, if she is truly honest with herself, that dirty bed behind the shabby curtain had filled her with a certain horror. She takes a teensy sip of her vile drink, rolls it around her tongue.

In front of her, on the sidewalk, life unfolds. French students stroll toward the Sorbonne. A mother feeds her toddler a pale wedge of pear. A passing Romany woman thrusts a tiny bouquet of lavender at her. She tries to refuse, but the woman is so insistent she feels in her pocket for some francs.

Under her fingers the lavender flowers are as soft as suede. *The hero as a struggling writer in Paris* is a male dream, she suddenly sees with clarity, the dream of somebody entirely free. But it is such an enchanting dream, so mesmerizing, that for a while she had succumbed to it. She had almost believed it could be hers.

DO PLEASE GO AWAY

A few days later she is sexually harassed. In France, sexual harassment is everywhere. Sometimes she and some girlfriends splurge on a café crème in one of the expensive Left Bank cafes, like Les Deux Magots. Sexual harassment is a favorite topic of conversation. All her friends have been flashed on the Metro. One guy, she learns, let it all hang out during commuter time. As the metro swayed down the track, his little wrinkled dick swayed from side to side. No one said a thing. Not the bankers, nor the shop assistants, nor the tourists. They just all stood there, gripping the straps that descended from the roof and staring out the windows as though their flickering reflections were the most entrancing things they had ever seen.

Her turn comes at last, on an escalator. Ascending up out of the labyrinth of Les Halles, she notices a man descending on the other side. He looks familiar, like an old friend of her father's, and her eyes linger, just for a second too long, on him. He feels her glance, of course. He turns at the bottom of the stairs, and comes up after her, so as she steps out into the sunlight he is on her heels. Would she like to join him for a drink, he asks in French. No, she wouldn't, thank you.

But the game is on; he follows her, insistent. "Why not? Why not? Just a quick one?"

"You are very kind," she finds herself saying, "but no." She is walking faster now, trying to keep to the main roads, with this person, this disconcerting amalgam of a man she once knew, and a pest, persistent at her shoulder.

"How about a hotel then? For a quick fuck. I know one around here. Come on, just a quick one."

The heat is rising in her but also a terror. She begs, in her polite schoolgirl French. "Please, won't you leave me alone? Do go away!"

"You are very beautiful," he tells her. "I can't help myself," and with this he strokes the end of her ponytail, just where it rests against her spine in a pale curve. "Just a quick screw. I'm good. I'll show you."

She is running now, damning herself for wearing these purple pixie boots with their ridiculous little heels. "Go away," she pants. "Please go away!" And into her mind swims the thought—why don't I swear at him? She knows those words, in French, but for some unfathomable reason, nothing comes out. Not even the English ones, which she should at least be comfortable with. At last they reach the Rue de Rivoli, the squat familiarity of Notre Dame's western façade to her left, filling her with relief. She glances over her shoulder. The man has dropped back, is skulking near a magazine stand, still watching her. She runs on, sweat trickling between her breasts, over the Isle de la Cité and under the linden trees with their gorgeous visceral scent. She does not stop running until she gets home. Her hand is quivering as she opens the door, the key will barely go in. Once inside, she throws the bolts, then pitches herself on the floor and tears off her boots.

Recounting the story to the girls, they all have a good giggle. She laughs along—in fact, she makes it sound almost amusing, the man ridiculous, a figure of fun. But the whole incident plays on her mind. Why could she not fight back? And why was it her he chose?

At home, she practices in front of the mirror. She firms her jaw. She narrows her eyes. She sets her shoulders. And she tells herself to go and #*$@! herself again and again and again, until the words become denuded of meaning, become shells, fluttering from her mouth like soulless things.

SALES GIRL

She gets a job as a sales girl at Hermès. Each day she walks across the bridge to the Rue St. Honoré where she changes into her yellow uniform. She has been allocated to the scarf counter. As the only natural English speaker, it is her job to deal with the Americans and their endless demands, and the Japanese. Day after day she faces another Japanese girl, who reads to her incomprehensibly from a phrase book. They all want the same thing, the scarf that the new Japanese princess wore, with its rose-pink silk, the classic pattern of stirrup, bridle.

The silk rushes like water through her hands. She folds, flips, molds it. Into a headscarf, bandana, a pussycat neck-bow, a belt, an accoutrement for the handle of a handbag. She is a wizard, a genius; by the end of her show she has an audience: five, six Japanese women, all beaming and bowing at her. They must have the scarf! A card is handed over, and the silk square is wrapped in a tangerine tissue-lined box, sealed with a caramel ribbon.

In the evening, as light transforms the Seine into an electrum ribbon, she crosses the bridge back to her flat. Her legs are weary from standing all day, and in the crevices of her brain, little dust balls of Japanese tumble around. She thinks of all those scarves she has sold being opened in hotel rooms across the city, that cool, thick silk pressed against skin. It was not something she ever anticipated putting on her resume, but she has become, she realizes with slight surprise, a Purveyor of Dreams.

One night, very late, as she rushes home by herself, nervous in the dark, she sees a unicorn walk right through the wall of the Musée de Cluny. She assumes she must be seeing things, but a young guy, wrapped in a plaid blanket and camped out on the corner, beckons her over. He is filthy, his eyes hollow pits, the crotch of his pants stained dark.

"Cigarette?" he asks. She shakes her head to say, *I'm sorry, I don't smoke,* but he forages under his blanket and pulls out two hand-rolled spliffs. He holds out one to her, and she takes it from him, touching as little of the thing as she can. He lights his up. A plume of fragrant smoke pours from his mouth. His gums are black, his teeth little shards of potato chip embedded within them.

"You saw it?"

"What?"

"The unicorn."

She stares at him.

"Don't deny it. I was watching you. I saw your face." He leans back against the wall, inhales again. "It is because of that shitty unicorn I sit here night after night."

"Why?" she asks.

"A photo," he says, and with that he pulls out a camera, an Instamatic. "I need a fucking photo. You know how much I'll get for it? A photo of a unicorn?"

She shakes her head.

He leers up at her, suddenly wary. "If I tell you, I never want to see you again. This is my turf. You get it?"

She nods.

"Four thousand. Maybe five for a good one. Enough to go to Africa."

"Africa?"

"Tanzania. You know it? Lake Natron. You should see the flamingos there. Pink clouds of them flying everywhere. They get pink like that from eating the algae. The algae in the lake. I saw this documentary on it, and I told myself one day I am going to get out of this crappy place and live there. Live the dream, you know. But that fucking unicorn. Every time I almost get a photo something happens. Car screws it up, or the light is wrong, or the photo just comes out blank." He shuts his eyes.

She waits a moment or two to see if he has more to say, but he seems to have gone to sleep. A light rain has begun to fall, fine as mist; under the lights, the drops sparkle like ground glass on her sleeves. She walks home through the Latin Quarter, where in the restaurants the desserts are laid out like jewels, the diamond-cut baklavas, the crescent-shaped cookies studded with pistachios.

The next day, she passes the guy again. He is asleep in his sleeping bag. On his temple is a horseshoe-shaped scar that she had not seen during the night. The skin of the scar is puckered, gray, and ugly, but below it his face is quite handsome, the curve of his nose fine. Holding her breath because, frankly, he reeks, she slides the spliff between two of his smoke-stained fingers and heads on.

DOGS

In May, she goes to see *Reservoir Dogs* with a friend. It is a very late showing, and by the time they get there she is already tired. The cinema is packed, the air warm and permeated with that inimical French scent: cigarette smoke with powerful top notes of sweat. There are interminable ads. When the movie starts she cannot follow it.

Mr. Blue, Mr. Black, fuck this, fuck that.

Her eyes will not stay open, they keep dripping shut. She slips into a fog of disjointed dreams.

Her friend pokes her. "Do you want to leave?"

She shakes her head. Oh, God, she would love to go, of course, but how can she? Her friend has so wanted to see this film—she cannot desert her. The movie rolls on. *Mr. Pink, Mr. White, whatever.* She follows the subtitles for a few minutes, and then sleep grabs her once more.

"Wake up! Wake up!" It is her friend, needling her again. She opens her eyes. On the screen a man is having his ear sawn off.

"Can we please leave now?" her friend whispers hotly into her hair.

They escape through an exit door into a cool night.

Moonlight gropes between the leaves of a plane tree, silvers, in snatches, its trunk. It is nearly twelve and yet the boulevard is still thronged with people. Her friend pulls a pack of Marlboros out of her pocket and lights one, her dusky Asian lips cupped like a calyx around the end. "That was awful," her friend says.

"Seemed so," she agrees, "but I was asleep for most of it."

"You were totally annoying," her friend tells her. "I wanted to leave ages ago. The guy next to me was jerking off under his coat the whole time. I kept trying to get you to wake up. What kind of guy does that? Jerk off in *Reservoir Dogs*?"

For a moment they just stare at each other, and then they start laughing. It is all they can do faced by this. They laugh until their ribs hurt, and then, high on the craziness of it all (and because it is getting late), they run down the sidewalk toward the metro, dodging between the pedestrians. Her friend's hair rises behind her head like the wing of bat, like a river of black water.

THE GREAT MOSQUE OF PARIS

Soon after, she visits the hamam at the Great Mosque of Paris, with a friend. The mosque is a twenty-minute walk away, but she sees it from afar, standing out among the flat-topped buildings like some exotic flower, a hibiscus perhaps. It is a quiet part of town, this section of the Fifth, grey, almost ghostly. Nearby, Rilke's panther wends endless circles, and the houses are barred and shuttered despite the warm spring day.

They check in with a man wearing a fez. Yes, they will have everything, the whole caboodle. They undress in the locker room, and then, quite naked barring a tiny towel and a cup of soap, they pass into the first room of the baths. The place is packed with women. The cadence of Arabic rises and falls through the air. She feels on edge, conscious of her nudity, her thin hips and small, pointed breasts. All around, bathers sprawl in the warmth, their scalps plastered with henna, their great blowsy bodies, with pendulous bosoms and stomachs, flowing like wax in the heat. They make their way down tiled corridors of swirling steam until they reach the final chamber, where the air is white and her skin burns. She sits on the edge of a pool, dips her feet in the frigid water. It is too hot to speak.

Time slides by. She half dozes, resting on a mosaic bench. She feels the gathering of herself, as though she is folding inward. Her nakedness starts to matter less. Across the way, two middle-aged women wash each other with zeal, the steam around them a milky rainbow. After a while, she is called in for her scrub. She is laid on a wooden bench and an Amazon, bare to the waist, attacks her with steel wool, until, like a snake inching out of its skin, she is born anew.

She is reunited with her friend in the relaxing room, where they sip mint tea from gold glasses. The room is octagonal, with more stained-glass windows and a dome rising high above. A massage table stands in the center. One by one, women are called up. When it is her turn, she finds she has lost all her shame. She lies there in her brave new skin as, all around, women drink tea and eat baklava. And when she turns over, so the masseuse can do her front, she notices that high above, from a balcony beneath the dome, faces are looking down. She does not care.

ARC DE TRIOMPHE

She drives into Paris for the first and last time. The French envision the Arc de Triomphe as a star radiating in all its glory from the summit of the Champs-Elysée, but in motoring terms it is a black hole. Approach in a car and you will be sucked in.

She and a friend drive down from Brussels. They plan to arrive late, imagining the roads will be quiet, but driving up to the sepulchral arch, she sees to her horror the glow of the traffic.

Her friend is pale with terror. She is quite cold. And yet, somehow, they survive. Her approach is fearless; she slows down, slips to second gear, then tears in, the car bucking and leaping beneath her. The traffic inside the circle must yield—it is the law—and to her amazement, it does. The journey within is galactic. They travel at warp speed, her tiny car an emerald blur amid the flashing lights, the roar. And then, before they can blink, they are cast out. They find themselves trundling at thirty mph down an avenue of pollarded horse chestnut trees. Ahead of her on the Place de la Concorde, where the guillotine once performed its grisly duty, a great glittering Ferris wheel turns against a velvet sky. Paris at night is so damn beautiful it makes her chest ache.

PONT DES ARTS

Twenty years later, she crosses the Pont des Arts with her husband. Beneath their feet, and visible through the wooden slats, the Seine glides silent. Padlocks have been clipped onto the railings, most engraved, some not. There are big ones, small ones, combination locks, and locks that have obviously been locked and then had the key dropped below into the water. It is quite an eyesore and a keen illustration of humanity's lack of imagination, but also, in its way, beautiful: a great unanimous declaration of love.

She and her husband lean against the railing and look west, to where the Eiffel Tower extends into the sky. The locks rub against her thighs. She holds her husband's hand. Paris, that great paper-maché confection, with its infinite layers of history and memory lying pressed against each other, unfolds out before them. She feels as though she has stood here a thousand times before. As they turn to go, a man drops to his knees in front of a woman and proposes. People clap. She starts to laugh. "Lets get out of here," she whispers and together, running as she used to, she and her husband leap down the stairs to the Left Bank, and make their way home.

AVRAM KLINE
YOUTH

Near the bathroom, he sets down his baby like a tub

of popcorn. Someone takes it.

This scenario resembles the life of anemones—

wavy opening and closing, tentacles sheltering a clownfish.

In Maryland a line-cook shoves a claw up the new dishwasher's

behind. Initiations vary.

We shuck four thousand oysters before we know we're killing them. No one tells us.

We shuck them, opening them like peanut butter jars. We hear them sipping.

In a flyer for London, a girl studies voice and has visions of flounder.

Blue shines in her. I am a young

man from Mexico City scrubbing and slicing a jumbo shrimp

that soon goes down a celebrity. Intimacy happens

too anonymously for science.

AVRAM KLINE

THE LAST RECORDED SPEECH OF PANCHO VILLA

At dusk the press drew near his desk
in the courtyard. The words of Pancho
Villa were these: Wayward hairs

have taken the bridge of my nose.
My bachelor face is a field
of beds and fallen trees. They say
Pancho screwed his eyes, tapped
his pipe and reached for an index
card. Chihuahua, enter

this dream as a moonbeam,
leave me to a quincunx
of cloud so I may sleep a celebrity.
I'm ready for death. For now,

my heart craves captivity.
My heart, a white bird in this net.

Pancho Villa clutched his breast,
then rose. The press let out a gasp.
Headlights of blue calcimine
flickered from the lot. He excused

himself. I excuse myself, he said.
The chauffeur opened the door
of the Dodge for Pancho Villa.
He set Pancho's Moviola in the trunk
and took him out to sea.

AVRAM KLINE

CHICAGO

When celebrity wears off they tunnel in.
Porters of Burnham handle the thighs,
Indians line the lounge with timber.

Natalie Cole arrives late.
The bed in her suite hasn't been turned
down, so I pull the duvet, fold the corner

of the sheet into a triangle, place a mint
on the triangle, fluff the pillows and restack
them decoratively. I dim the lights, too.

She proffers a hand and asks my name
and says to me, You will not leave me.
You will stay with me. You will touch

my nimbus. Little Richard mans the dais,
as bulls await his order, wanting to breed.
Little Richard is rattling. Rail

tracks are sleeves and I am undressing.
We pass Jean Baptiste Point du Sable beside
a lakeside cottage where he learnt the native

tongue and felled the trees and settled

the mouth of the river. He is reaching into

an ox. He is saying, I'm done with Indians,

I'll do as I please. *This is my beast, my beast.*

Recognize me? The aquifer holds my name.

Brittlebush feeds the current, then comes piñon.

MR. JENNY PERDIDO

CATHY DAY

One dark night in her 40th year on this planet and her third year on Match.com, Jenny Perdido decides that the time has come for drastic measures. Even though she's a professor of history at Johns Hopkins, she downgrades the occupation on her dating profile from "professor" to "teacher," and she changes her search criteria from men who make between $50,000 and $80,000 a year (which is what she makes) to include all men who make at least $25,000 a year.

This is how Alan pops up on her radar.

Alan's profile says that he is a college graduate and a trained chef, but on their first date at a seafood restaurant overlooking the Inner Harbor, the truth comes out: actually, he's a temp at a law office that specializes in foreclosures. He confesses this just after they order drinks. "It makes my soul itch, but still, it's better than working in a kitchen," he says. When Jenny asks why it's better, Alan points to the swinging doors at the back of the restaurant and says, "It's a busy night, and when it's all over, everyone on the other side of that wall will need a smoke or a drink or a hit or a pill to calm down, and I can't do that anymore." He sighs and takes a drink of water. "My motto these days is 'No drama,' and kitchens are nothing but drama."

"Foreclosing on people's homes is dramatic," Jenny says quietly.

"Well, I don't talk to the homeowners. I shuffle papers and make phone calls and fax things. It's pretty calming, actually, and the pay's okay, which is how I fund my reading habit. It'd be a great job if you didn't have to think about what you're doing to people." He takes off his glasses and rubs the bridge of his nose. "Well, enough about that," he says. "Tell me, what grade do you teach?"

Jenny taps nervously on the stem of her glass of sauvignon blanc. "Well, grade sixteen and seventeen, I guess."

Alan looks at her funny for a second, and then she sees him do the math in his head. "Ah," he says. "You're a prof."

She watches Alan's face closely, waiting for the expression that often comes into men's eyes when she says what she does and where she works. Over the last three years, Jenny has developed a name for this expression: "The Curtain Falls."

But magically, Alan's face fills with light. She thinks, "The Curtains Part."

He peppers her with questions about her classes and the book she's writing about minstrelsy and the American circus. He leans forward on his elbows. "That's fascinating. How did you become interested in that?"

"I was born in a circus town. Lima, Indiana."

"I remember watching a documentary about minstrel shows in college…"

"*Ethnic Notions*?"

"That's it!" Alan smiles. "Tell me more," he says.

And oh my God, Jenny has so much to say.

For the next two months, they talk about everything in the world except what they do for a living.

And then Alan moves in.

You need to know this: Jenny has been divorced and living alone for nine years. This is a long and lonely stretch of time, and as much as she wants another human being around, the reality of it actually scares her shitless. He won't understand how much time she needs. That a closed door doesn't mean that she's being rude or neglectful. No, he'll knock softly—like her dad, like her ex-husband, like all her ex-boyfriends—and ask "What are you doing? Are you almost done?"

Why don't they ever understand that she'll *never* be done—that she'll always be working on something, writing it down, following this or that train of thought, digging around, thinking with her fingers—and that this is exactly how she wants her life to be.

But Alan—oh, Alan—understands perfectly. Because he wants *exactly* the same thing. His coming disrupts nothing, costs nothing. No monthly bills arrive for him, and she asks,

"Did you forget to forward your mail?"

"No."

"Surely you're paying off *something*. Everyone's in debt."

Alan laughs and says no, he paid off everything he owed when he got sober and started living his simple, drama-free life.

But one Friday, Alan loses his temp job at the foreclosure mill.

On Saturday, they avoid talking about this.

On Sunday morning, he says, "Look Jenny, we don't need the money. You've got an incredibly stressful job. Two jobs! Teaching and writing. I can take care of you. I can take care of everything so you can do those jobs better. Climb the ladder. I'll throw great dinner parties. It'll be like *Mad Men*, but you're Don and I'm Betty."

Jenny buries her head in the crook of his neck. He smells like garlic. "But I'm Peggy," she says.

"Maybe in 1960, you're Peggy. Spinster working girl. But in 2009, Peggy marries Betty." Alan laughs and strokes her hair.

"I don't want Betty to give up her career for me."

"What career?"

"You're a model, I think."

Alan peeks under the duvet. "I'm definitely not a model."

"You're a chef."

"I don't want to cook for anybody but us."

"This is all too retro," she says.

Alan takes her head in his hands and looks her straight in the eye. "Marry me. I want to be Mr. Jenny Perdido."

She looks into his grey eyes, and then she looks away. "My mom thought she wanted to be Mrs. Ethan Perdido. She tried to be a Betty until I was fourteen."

Alan knows this story—how her mom's discontent haunted their house, how she disappeared from time to time, how her cheating was always discreet and always politely ignored until the horrible day Jenny caught her in the act and it couldn't be ignored anymore, how her mother left in the middle of the night and was never heard from again—and Alan knows that the last thing her mother said to her was "Marry yourself first, Jenny," which she did.

"I'm not your mom," Alan says. "I'm thirty eight. I've lived plenty. Long enough to know that I'm man enough to be a wife, whatever that means. And be happy about it. No regrets."

The house is very quiet, and Jenny says, "Give me some time to think about it."

"A week," Alan says. "Let me show you how it can be."

Alan always makes something special on Sunday night. This week, it's poached orange roughy with a cranberry-pomegranate-lemongrass-cream sauce with quinoa and broccoli.

And she asks herself, *What would I have had for dinner before meeting Alan?*

Answer: Fancy Boiled Tortellini from a Plastic Bag and a Jar of Mama Mia's Gourmet Puttanesca.

On Monday, Jenny's best friend from college calls to see how things are going and find out what Alan "does."

Jenny says things are fine. Alan's been temping.

She doesn't mention the proposal.

She goes to campus to teach her classes, and Alan writes for awhile and reads and runs errands. When she gets home, she finds veal stew on the stove.

And she asks herself, *What would I have had for dinner on a night like tonight before Alan?*

Answer: Quizno's Sub in a Paper Sleeve, purchased near the bus stop.

On Tuesday, Jenny's best friend from graduate school emails and asks how things are going and to find out what Alan "does."

Jenny writes that things are fine. Alan's been temping.

She still doesn't mention the proposal.

Her friend emails right back and says, "I don't want to be a Debbie Downer, but aren't you worried he just wants a Sugar Mama?"

She goes to campus and Alan writes and reads and gets her car serviced. When she gets home from seven hours of conferences, she finds almond-herb crusted halibut with polenta and roasted vegetable ragout. After dinner, he shoos her out of the kitchen, and she goes upstairs to write a little.

And she asks herself, *What would I have had for dinner on a night like tonight before Alan?*

Answer: a Ginormous Bowl of Buttered Popcorn with a Side of Bourbon.

On Wednesday, Jenny's father calls and asks how things are going and to find out what Alan "does."

Jenny says things are fine. Great even. She says (vaguely) that Alan is between jobs and that someday, they might get married. Maybe.

Her father says, "Remember what happened with Roger." Her ex-husband.

"Alan isn't anything like Roger."

"Good," he says. "Are you coming home for Christmas?"

She goes to campus, and Alan spends the day installing closet organizers. When she gets home, he's made chicken piccata, risotto, asparagus, and a green salad with pine nuts and balsamic vinaigrette.

And she asks herself, *What would I have had for dinner on a night like tonight before Alan?*

Answer: One-Pot Couscous with Frozen Mixed Vegetables, topped with Pre-Grated Cheddar Cheese.

Jenny invented this dish when she taught at Eastern Plains College in Emporia, Kansas, her first teaching job. She moved there after grad school with Roger, her then-husband and Trailing Spouse, who'd also applied for the job she landed and instead ended up adjuncting at Eastern Plains while Jenny rode the tenure track. His abject misery filled their apartment like Sarin gas. One day—near the end—Jenny came home from campus an hour early. She had a colleague with her who wanted to borrow their turkey roaster. They surprised Roger, who stood in the living room holding a can of Pledge. (She'd asked him to take over the cleaning duties; she taught four classes, and he taught two.) Startled, Roger saw them glance down at the dust rag in his hand and blushed, like he'd been caught wearing women's underwear.

Later, he said to her, "I wish you would have called first."

And a few weeks later, he said, "I think I might hurt myself."

And a few weeks after that, he left Kansas for a mid-term replacement position in Toledo.

Jenny faced the six-month winter alone, eating One-Pot Couscous every night for dinner. Because it was easy. Because you could eat it on a paper plate. Because Roger took all the white Pottery Barn dishes they'd gotten at their wedding. And their Calphalon cookware. And the turkey roaster. Even when they divorced a year later, she was still eating One-Pot Couscous on paper plates every night. Because she couldn't bear to go out and replace any of the wedding gifts he'd taken.

On Thursday, Jenny goes to a lecture on campus. At the reception, her colleagues—whose spouses all have jobs of equal prestige to their own—ask her how things are going and what Alan "does."

Jenny says things are fine, but there's an edge to her voice that she can't smooth away. She says, "I suppose you could say that Alan works for me. He's a homemaker. He makes our home," which causes everyone in her small circle to grow very quiet and avoid her eyes.

Later, someone comes up to her privately and pats her on the back, saying, "Feminist theorists have long argued that the gendered dichotomization of social life constitutes the very cornerstone from which women's social contributions are all too often mislabeled as 'non-work.'"

Jenny's eyes fill with tears and she says, "Thank you soooo much."

She leaves the reception early and comes home to jerk pork chops, fried sweet plantains, sweet potatoes with scallion/ginger/lime butter, and papaya relish.

And she asks herself, *What would I have had for dinner on a night like tonight before Alan?*

Answer: University Catering Service Mini-Quiches with Fruit Tray Garnishes and Toothpick-Skewered Cheese Cubes, finished with Many Small Plastic Glasses of Wine.

On Friday, Jenny goes to campus for a meeting—a terrible, awful meeting—and when she arrives home in tears, she finds Moroccan chicken with couscous and roasted zucchini. To take her mind off the Terrible Meeting, Alan tells her how he learned to make the prune sauce for the Moroccan chicken from a chef named Mohammed, who threw pans at his head and screamed "If you cannot do eet, you cannot do eet!"

Alan shrugs his shoulders. "I could not do eet anymore without drinking myself stupid at the end of the day. So here I am. With you."

And she asks herself, *What would I have had for dinner on a night like tonight before Alan?*

Answer: Edible food products eaten absently at the kitchen counter while rehashing the Terrible Meeting in her head. Always-on-hand cocktail party supplies (chips and salsa, hard salami, Triscuits, martini olives, and gherkins) which could be inserted into her mouth within fifteen seconds of decision to eat. Taste, color, texture, nutritional value—irrelevant. A swallowable material to silence the gnawing ache in her abdomen so she could get back to work and prove to everyone at the Terrible Meeting that she was not in over her head, and if need be, she would work all weekend to prove this.

On Saturday, Jenny and Alan spend the morning reading and writing, and in the afternoon, they walk to a seafood market to buy fresh scallops. He breaks out her never-used blender to make purees of sweet pea and red pepper, which he pours into squeeze-bottles. "This," he says drawing green and red zig zags on the plate "is jizz. And these," he says, garnishing with chopped parsley, "are sprinkles." He places the red plate before her with a flourish.

Perhaps it's the jizz and sprinkles that remind her not of the food on the plate, but the plate itself. Purchased years ago in Boston—which was after Kansas, but before Baltimore. She taught then at a small college with an adjunct named Tanya who was married to a full professor, a Big Star. One day, Tanya asked "Oh please, will you take me to Target? I need diapers and paper towels and laundry detergent. And I don't know how to drive." Jenny picked her up, and Tanya cried all the way there. "He never helps," she said. "I have to do it all. Everything so he can work. I had to *beg* him to watch the baby for a few hours so I could come with you. He wanted me to bring her with *me* so *he* could work. He never helps so I can do *my* work." That's when Jenny told Tanya about Roger and the can of Pledge. Tanya sighed and looked out the car window. "Do you remember the video for the song "Imagine"? I wanted *that*. John and Yoko walk in the park, and then they go inside and make things. But what I never realized was that I wanted to be John, the one sitting in a dark room at the piano. I didn't want to be Yoko. I didn't want to be the one who opens the shutters to let in the light."

"Neither did I," Jenny said.

"Neither did your ex-husband," Tanya said.

"Neither does yours."

And then they laughed. Bitterly.

Sitting now in her Baltimore kitchen across from the man she knows she'll marry, Jenny wonders how long it's been since she thought of Tanya, who killed herself a few weeks later, and for months after that, Jenny could think of nothing but that day at Target, every moment from start to finish. Like how she confessed to Tanya that she'd been divorced for two years and was still eating off paper plates. Tanya marched her right over to the house wares section. "Everybody says white plates are better for presentation, but I like these red ones." Tanya turned a plate over in her hands. "These will give you something to look forward to after a long, hard day."

THE STUDY OF NAMES

LUKE ROLFES

According to my little brother, the name Nathan Roth Rolfes is a hideous balloon hitched to his wrist that can't be untied. He threatened my parents for years, even as a finger-pointing kid standing in the hallway at bedtime.

"When I turn eighteen," he declared. Teenage Mutant Ninja Turtles pajamas. "Nathan Roth Rolfes dies. In his place, a new man will be born."

My brother's middle name is my maternal grandfather's last name; it's German, just like Rolfes. If you Google the Roth family crest, you see a shield draped in red tapestry featuring a single black crow. It might be a raven, but there's no such thing as a raven in central Iowa where Nathan and I grew up.

The Rolfes family crest is a shield flanked by black and white plumages, but our shield has three crows on it. I've always considered myself a Rolfes more than a Roth. Rolfes is my name, after all, and Roth is the name my mom used to have before she married my dad. It's probably different for my brother. When he hears the name Roth, he thinks of himself. Two surnames rolled into one, two family crests. I'm as much Roth as he is, but I don't have the label. I don't have as many crows.

My first name comes from my paternal grandmother's last name, Luken. The boys around Le Mars, Iowa, would call the Luken boys "Luke" during games of horseshoes and kick the can, so when my grandmother hears my name, she imagines the faces of her red-haired brothers, dust and perspiration pressed into their creased skin. Instead, she gets me. My hair is the color of sunbaked grass, but I have pine needle eyes, just like all the Luken boys. Just like my brother.

✳

During the summer my brother turned eighteen, I worked for the Iowa Department of Natural Resources. One of my responsibilities was to mow the grass behind the pole shed. We had these old Ford tractors with cyclone, pull-behind mowers. I would drive in awkward circles, letting the clutch out slowly under my boot, and the mower would suck up and then vomit out grass and dirt. Sitting all alone on my tractor, I contemplated what my brother's best friend Mike had told me earlier that afternoon at the beach. It was taking a while to sink in.

After weed-eating the dam, I had gone to the concession stand at the marina (where

Mike and Nathan worked) for a cold drink. I sat on the picnic table, face deep in Pepsi and ice, when I noticed Mike seated next to me, staring out like he had a bone to pick with the lake.

"Foolish," he said, as a way of starting conversation.

"What's foolish?"

"Your brother," Mike said. "If I were you, I'd be pretty mad about all this. I'd be pissed, actually."

I nodded, a bit confused, but nodded anyway. Mike seemed distraught—stomach pouched, back hunched—like he wanted to get something off his chest. He was, as were all boys who worked at the marina, shirtless and bearded.

"It's not like it's that bad," he said. "I'm sure your parents are going to talk him out of it. I mean, he kept saying he was going to do it, but who really thinks a guy is actually going to follow through with it. I'm not going to change what I call him. That would be stupid. I mean, you get used to calling a guy a particular thing, and if that changes, the guy sort of changes, or, at least, the way you think about the guy changes. I guess you're pretty mad. I'd sure be mad if I were you."

I chewed on some ice and started to wonder if my brother had finally done what he had been threatening to do for years: change his middle name to something less awkward, less "last name sounding" and more "middle name" sounding. Something vanilla.

"Jay," Mike said. He shook his head. "That's such a gay name. I can't even really talk about it."

And there it was. Jay. I cared, but I wasn't angry. It was a well-known fact that my brother thought his middle name to be "one of the gayest names in history," and he was simply taking action. Nathan Roth Rolfes produced no lyrical acrobatics. No girl would doodle those sixteen letters on the wisp of her forearm. My brother told me once that his name represented three dumpy cows stuck in the fence. Nate. Roth. Rolfes. Cow, cow, cow.

I never thought my brother would put something more on the government change of name form. Instead of writing Nathan Jay Rolfes in the "what you shall henceforth be called" blank, he wrote the name "Nathan Jay Riley." He may as well have written "Nathan Spaceman Alcatraz."

When Mike finally wriggled the words "Jay Riley" out of his mouth, they fell like dead squids onto the deck of the picnic table. There they were: alien, otherworldly. I stood, unconsciously, and stared out across the water. Nathan Jay Riley. The glare off the lake was brutal, but I could make out the colorful shapes of Obie sailboats bouncing in slow pulses on the waves. Nathan Jay Riley. My brother was on one of those boats. He was smiling like an asshole, giving a sailing lesson. *Nathan Jay Riley.* Which boat was he on, though? The yellow one? The blue? Somewhere, on one of those boats, my brother was laughing. I was sure of it. I could hear him in my mind. Where was he? Why couldn't I see him?

"You're taking this well," Mike said. "I'd be pretty mad."

✳

I'd like to think my brother and I connect now, but I can't be sure. He was the Best Man at my wedding, and we hug when we haven't seen each other in a while. I must disappoint him in some way. If we go hiking, and there is a log stretched over a dizzying, bottomless canyon, he'll raise both arms like a dancer and step foot-over-foot across the length of it. When he reaches the other side, he'll yell for me to come over. I'll look at the log and shake my head. In many ways, he has adopted the bravado of the older brother, and I'm the young one putting my face down and submitting.

Maybe part of the problem is he never seems to age. My brother tells me about how, several months ago, he put his hands on the stump of the oldest tree in the world, a nearly 5000 year old bristlecone pine that was cut down by a graduate student in the California desert. The student had no idea that the tree he felled was actually the oldest living organism on the planet. My brother said he felt the tree's pain travel up his arms and into his heart, and it was all he could do not to throw up—just think: a person on this earth for a quarter century stupidly stamping out a life that had spanned five millennia. My brother is describing all this to me in detail, but I'm picturing him, eight years old, crying his eyes out at the stump of our favorite climbing tree which had succumbed to heart rot. The dead tree lay on its side, our dad's chainsaw next to its trunk, still warm. "What have you done?" my brother screamed at our father's upturned hands. "You've killed the only tree I've ever loved."

Nathan didn't like me much when we were kids. He may or may not hate the man I have become. He's into health and treading lightly across the earth's skin, the Green movement and conservation, and I simply feel good about myself if I manage to recycle or drink less than three Coke Zeros in a given day. My life has followed the standard trajectory of an American boy from the Midwest. I went to college. I got married. I had a child. My brother's life was different. Itinerant, maybe. Picaresque. He still doesn't know what he wants out of life. He still doesn't know where he is going or how he will get there.

"There's gotta be some purpose," he said to me once, "some reason I eat healthy and exercise. There has to be a purpose for me wanting to live a long time."

✳

"I'm not going to talk about it," my dad said on the cell phone when I called him on my way back to the shop. My mother gave me a similar response when I called her. You'd think there was a prize to see who could hang up the phone the fastest.

I climbed aboard the mower back at the shop. Well, shit, I thought. With all these people not talking about my brother's name change, I was free to just sit and stew in my own thoughts. When a twenty one year old gets upset, he jumps to conclusions. He iterates and slippery slopes. It's chaos theory in action. My brother's new name changed the starting conditions. Nathan Jay Riley flapped his wings in China, and we got snow in Iowa instead of sunshine.

I feared the sight of him. I knew I would see him tonight, when I opened the back door of my parents' house. He'd be lying on the couch with a bag of chips on his belly, the flicker of the television across his face. Would it still be him? My brother? Would I even recognize him, or would he have changed, the way a person changes when they get their first real job or find out they are going to have a baby. And why did he pick Riley? What does Riley have to do with anything? What would I tell somebody years from now when I showed up at my brother's apartment? "Yeah, he's my brother. No, we do have the same parents. It's complicated." Nathan's nephew (Baby Jack) wasn't born yet, but I imagined explaining it all to him. "Uncle Nate doesn't have your last name. No, it's not because he got married. I don't know. He picked it out of a book."

*

The year after I learned to drive, my brother was hit by a car. His two best friends ran red-faced and screaming my name down the street. Nathan had turned purple, they said. He wasn't breathing. By the time we piled out of my Corolla, EMT's had surrounded the sleeping shape of my only sibling.

A guy in my class whose car had knocked my brother into a bush was punching dents into the car door, looking at nobody. The passenger, another guy from my high school, was trying to hug me in a sort of apologetic, grief-confused daze. My brother's two friends were calling the driver a stupid asshole—they were saying somebody ought to run him over. I don't remember the level of my fear. I just remember staring down at my brother's scraped face and thinking, "Wake up, damn it. Open your eyes." The EMT's were cutting his clothes off with scissors.

"What time is it?" Nathan said suddenly, eyelids flickering back to life.

I should have asked him a question. I don't know why I didn't. For all I knew he could have died right there on the street with me staring at him, but I said, "Nathan, you're okay," and hearing his name out loud made me feel like I could suddenly breathe.

*

So there I am sitting on this stupid mower, my legs vibrating into pudding and my face baking into crust, and I'm just spinning in big, arced circles behind the shop, trying to swipe the strips of grass that I keep missing, not really making any progress.

I'm not dramatic. I don't want it to hurt. I really don't want it to, but I can't help that it does. It isn't a big deal, is it? It isn't like my brother suddenly disappeared and I was never going to see him again. It isn't like he actually died there on the road when my classmate ran him over with the car.

But it is a big deal, maybe. You remember all the people who have come before you, and the significance of a name snowballs. I can't help but think about my great, great grandfather. He was a part of the German navy, and when they docked in New York City, he just stepped off the boat and started to run. I can imagine him setting foot on the new world's cobblestones, so long on the boat, but now land—real land—beneath his feet. Suddenly, my great, great grandfather felt the urge to sprint. There wasn't a gunwale to stop his progress. There were streets in front of him, and they led to homes, and roads, and train tracks, and eventually, the farmlands of Middle America. Everything was in front of him: a wife, children, grandchildren, their grandchildren.

"Goddamnit, Rolfes," the *Deutsche Marine* captain yelled, but my great, great grandfather didn't hear him. He was already gone.

And that was how the Rolfeses made their way onto this land—some big German dude screaming at my great, great grandfather on the pier. Maybe the captain even threatened to take a shot at old gramps with a Lugar. Maybe he just shrugged and bid him Auf Wiedersehen. Other Rolfeses came to America in different ways, but that was how our family arrived. I don't know how or why the Rileys showed up.

"No, Baby Jack, there aren't any crows on the Riley crest. There are two lions fighting over a severed human hand. No, I don't know why the lions want to eat the hand."

If I were brave enough, I may have asked my brother: What is it about the name Rolfes that you really don't like? Don't you want to be a part of this? Don't you want to be connected to Dad and our grandparents, and their grandparents before them? Don't you want to be like me? Even a little bit?

✳

I'd like to say the story has a happy ending. I'd like to say that Nathan came to his senses a week later, took a look in the mirror and said, "That's not Nathan Jay Riley. That's not me." But that didn't happen

My mom's dad found out about the name change. My mom was cleaning his house, and she let it slip in front of him. Needless to say, he wasn't pleased.

"Give me the phone," he said.

I'm not sure what exactly my grandfather said to Nathan. The details are cloudy. I imagine the conversation involved a deep discussion of my grandfather's thoughts on what a name means. A name, to him, was something more than what we called each other. A name, to him, was a way to identify his grandsons, all seven of us, a way he could recognize who was a part of his family and who wasn't. It's uncertain if my grandfather told Nathan that he was no longer technically his grandson, but he certainly implied that it was going to be damn hard to recognize him as a grandson if his name were Nathan Jay Riley.

It makes me sad to think about the short and unhappy life of Nathan Jay Riley. The next day my brother began the process of annulment, and his flash-in-the-pan name change was erased from historical record. Yes, my brother still carries around the name he hates, and, yes, it will probably one day grace the stone on his grave. Nathan Roth Rolfes. That's who he is. But that doesn't mean he has accepted the label as himself. That doesn't mean that he wears the name proudly, or even wants to be associated with the people who share his blood, our people, the "fam."

"You know what I like about you, Nathan," I told him once. "Out of all the people in the world, you're the one who is the most genetically similar to me."

"That's true," he said. "But you are taller."

And maybe the thing about us that doesn't change is the way we can fall into lockstep with our old roles from time to time. We still have the habit of announcing "blue team" as soon as somebody suggests a game of Pictionary. We still manage to fall asleep within twenty minutes of each other when we come home for the holidays. Maybe that's what being related is all about—the way you can recognize proximity as neither forced nor uncomfortable. It will be late at night, and Nathan will suddenly open the door with a bowl of homemade popcorn and two ice waters. We'll turn on the television to something that makes us laugh, and just sit there in the dark, two Rolfes brothers watching tv, laughing at the same jokes. The same as we did growing up. The same as we'll always do.

JENNA LE

TIBERIUS

(Inspired by Robert Graves's I, Claudius*)*

I am Tiberius, a dark man. My moods are dark
as the blood-soaked meat
of an ox slaughtered
to sate a pregnant woman's
unnatural hungers.

My mother is a ubiquitous woman,
pervasive as the odor
of rotting sheep's liver.

Since my boyhood,
she has hung around my neck
like a thirteenth pair of ribs,
narrowing my windpipe to the width of a ribbon.

She is cold-blooded, half-jellyfish,
half-giantess.
Her translucent skin
shows her tentacles
to be filled with green lymph.

I tried to hide from her, once....
Donning a suit of red bronze,
I played a game of camouflage with her,
pressing my body flush against the bole of a red pine.
But she managed to find me.

I tried to flee from her, once....
I followed the North Star
high into the Alps, into the barbarian climes of Germany.
But she captured me, and dragged me home.

The nadir was when she ripped me apart
from my loving wife of eight years:
casually,
the way someone tears the skin off an orange.

It was like the scene of a flaying:
my citrus blood
stank up the whole room.
And when my mother
jabbed her finger in the anus of the denuded fruit,
aborted seeds spilled everywhere.

JENNA LE

TIDAL BREATHING

There is a duck

patrolling the lake shore,

his seed-like eyes

gazing at the water

as it stretches away from us

like a pewter plate

on which the breezes clink like coins.

His gray cottony belly

drags along the shelves of stone.

Beneath the surface gloss

of his brown breastplate,

his puffed-out chest

harbors two separate fistfuls

of cold oxygen.

His lungs are more evolved, more efficient

than our human lungs,

circulating the diamond-bright

northern air

through a network of tiny tubes and valves

without waste

or sentiment.

It is so superior

to the way we mammals breathe:

our noisy ragged sobs,

our shallow tidal exhalations,

the way our soft fleshy noses

drag morsels of blue sky

into the dark zones

that border our red hearts.

How hard his beak seems,

like the warped yellow wood

of an attic piano.

How rock-hard

his green feathered skull.

JENNA LE NATIVITY

At the age of six, I was gripped

by a movie I saw

about a nubile girl

whose single-engine

plane, while farting

above a primeval forest

near the Equator,

bursts into flame.

This dour girl

is the sole survivor.

For the next decade,

she is condemned

to live utterly alone,

scrounging for edible

insects, erecting a hut

to deflect the heavy rains

and stave off

a fatal pneumonia.

Over time, she forms alliances

with certain fauna.

A herd of antlered

animals she never read about

in any book

befriends her.

Their pelts

are almost impossibly golden.

Their lustrous legs

are so graceful,

she wonders at first

if this is what

solitary girls hallucinate—

and maybe it is,

but in the wild

these questions of narrative plausibility

lose all meaning.

The girl becomes enamored

of these deer

that she's not sure really exist.

Say what you will

about feminism

and the onward march of civilization,

but in the wild

there's no feeling

except crude desire,

no middle ground
between death and estrus.

Her human characteristics
disappear. She is absorbed
into the creaturely herd.
Maybe this could have been averted
if she had had a pocket Bible,
the voiceover narrator theorizes...

Listen:
there is a myth
often told in this part of the world
about a human girl
who squats in a grove
and delivers
a baby boy with antlers.

Will you give it the lie?
You, whose feral face
asserts your ancestry?
You, whose moments of grace
bring to mind the stag
that fathered the impossible fawn?

JENNA LE

HAIKU

White men edit all

the top haiku magazines—

Pigeon poop on Basho's grave

JENNA LE

MY EYE DOCTOR

Today my ophthalmologist, who's been
happily married to an Anne Boleyn
lookalike for almost seven years,
sat me in his office chair and peered
into my eyes more deeply than my boyfriends
ever have. The little flashlight he deployed
to help with his reconnaissance
gave off the heat of twenty suns.

I felt exposed, as if he were my lover
appraising me, withholding his approval.
No lover was he, though: if you now asked him,
"What color were those eyes whose rays you basked in?
Can you remember that?", he'd be unable.
His motives, unlike love, were noble. Stable.

BOXES
DANIEL ENJAY WONG

Before I was even born, the people in my town built a box with no windows. On the front, a sign said, "No boys allowed."

My life began in there, along with others. It was the country, where streets had no lamps or sidewalks and there was only one kind of man. We raised ourselves in the dark, snaking towards the faintest light.

Every year at our town fair, there was farmer who sold square watermelons—he grew them in boxes, too. They used to be round until they reached the edges of the wooden crate that pushed their roundness into hard corners. I always wondered if that hurt them, but people would crowd around the tent in excitement. Standing sweaty together under the tarp, they'd watch but never buy. *Charming! Who knew you could do that to watermelons?*

My town is all edges and no curves.

The odd shapes were always home sick. *We don't know what it he's down with, but we're pushing fluids,* said our parents at family gatherings. We were prayers and condolences. Every morning before church when the staff greeted the congregation, the pastor would pass by me and squeeze my arm. Mother would talk about how sweet he was, but I think he was just checking to see if I was still soft.

Even without windows, there were still holes and cracks through which we could breathe. Some of us found that we didn't get in trouble late at night: in a car, in the basement, in the woods. We hid from the bright candy lights of cops and the glow from our parents' bedrooms. Our lights were off.

The pastor once said that these sick people could get better. All a man needed was will and Jesus would put a loving hand on him. Some of us believed it, but we'd never seen the ocean.

One day after church, a boy asked to see the pastor. I'd always known. The nuns sat him on the edge during Sunday school because he had shaky legs. He'd stare at me like he knew we were the same thing.

We weren't friends, but their family lived the next street over. His father's hand was on him but not to heal. I remember the pastor smiling, down on one knee like the boy was his son.

Then the town opened, snapped shut and I never saw him again.

*

The sky is clean. The sweep of morning rain has only left the purest things behind.

We are green bodies. Casey and I play

outside in my backyard. We dig through the dirt with our hands, fingertips raw from nails our mothers clipped too short. We are boys looking for answers.

I find a question instead. A small blue rock. Blue like something sweet and foamy—food coloring and milk. The rock is the same as Casey's eyes, with a spot in the center where the drop of blue starts to bloom.

Casey's eyes catch the rock in my open hand. His face lights up the same way as Mother's when she gathers offering. My mother is a collector. Our house is full of antiques, stiff furniture and more dolls than people. I like to think that I collect words, which isn't really the same, but collecting is the one thing I've inherited from my mother. She doesn't like to think she's given me anything else.

Casey leaps at me and grabs my wrists, growling. He has crazy eyes. We wrestle in the damp, our ears tickled by grassy stalks. I stretch the rock out of his reach, but after a few seconds, both our hands are empty.

I feel myself get hard in my overalls. As I reach down to cover myself, I realize that Casey isn't holding my wrists anymore.

Then our fingers are twisting together in the soil, earthworms coming out of wet earth to breathe.

*

Squeezing me tighter, Mother presses my face against her breasts as we pass the flashes and blares in front of our neighbor's house. I remember seeing half a blur of pink fabric and half a crowd of people staring.

I know I'm not supposed to look, so I lock my eyes shut inside my mother's safe. I feel the clinking of her metal Jesus on my head as we walk. On the way home, I stumble a few times. I can't see the rocks, the patches of grass in my way. I think Mother forgot she told me to shut my eyes because I step on her toe and she says, "Oh, for God's sake."

Mother later said that she always knew the neighbor was off. He was sick in the worst way. She said "sick" like she could taste him.

I decided that the only reason anyone would drink bleach was if he thought his mouth was a dirty drain.

The house is for sale now but no one will buy. The people in my town are afraid of private places. No one knew who he was, but they knew what he did. Maybe a piece of him is stuck to the floor of the shower or has seeped into the carpet. Someone mentions toilet seats.

After a long wait, the house gets tired. The tree in the front yard is overgrown, and a branch has broken through the man's bedroom window. The overgrown grass makes a big field that I want to run in, but Mother says rats are living in there. I imagine my bare feet trampling their tiny bodies, teeth and bones and little rat spines. I decide not to because I might kill a family.

As head of the church congregation, Mother volunteers to clean up the house. Others follow soon after. My mother wears bright red lipstick and sleeps on one side of a double bed. She says that working hard helps her forget about what's missing. It's the summer and she teaches vacation Bible school on the side. Doesn't feel like a vacation, she says, but it's God's work.

I wonder if I am complete.

Everyone makes a huge commotion about the cleaning, like some perilous jungle expedition. I watch my mother unload bottles of disinfectant from her car parked in front of the man's house. I take one when she isn't looking.

✳

All we can see is open space. The kind of open space that shocks your eyes and makes you blind.

Casey's truck is parked in a wooded clearing, where leaves keep the tires quiet. We lie on the empty bed. Rust is probably staining our shirts. Our faces sting, beer and sweat. Sunlight angles down through the trees and above us I can see mayflies swarming thick like smoke.

Shifting my body, I feel something crinkle in my back pocket. I reach inside and pull out something silver: an old note Casey scrawled on a gum wrapper. He wrote me a poem, a few lines that don't make much sense unless you were there.

I read the poem in my head. We write for fun but mostly to feel like we have something to say.

I turn to Casey's arm hair catching the sun. We are both fourteen. I think about this like I know what it means.

"You're like a spider's web—all wisp and uncertainty," I say. Feeling proud of the line, I enjoy a victory stretch. We think we are poets. The next big thing.

Church bells ring nearby. I think the mayflies get scared too, because they start to scatter in the light.

The bells remind us of where we are. Our minds have converged in the same place, but Casey is the first to say something. He's waited for me outside stained glass, watched my mother stride between walls of obedience with an offering basket.

"She knows. She'll send you there." He is thinking about the boy and his legs. Pastors, fathers and Gods.

I shake my head, refusing to believe.

✳

I remember turning sixteen because my birthday present was a plane ticket.

Mother bought cupcakes, chocolate ones that spell something together in sweet blue icing. Letters have been eaten, picked at, shared with the neighbors.

I'm staring at a boarding pass on the table while Mother sweeps around the kitchen, making little eager motions on cabinets or counters but not really doing anything. She chirps about how the church helped pay and how she'll manage just fine here alone. With Mother this way, it's hard to imagine her last week when she finally found the blue in me.

When I was still in the womb, the doctor

took one look at the swirl of ultrasound and said I was a girl. Without a doubt. He changed his mind later, but I think my mother would have been happy either way. Most people don't expect a third thing.

Mother snaps her fingers. "Just like that." She is talking about the therapy. "It'll flip you inside out." In the cabinet, she straightens the spice jars on their rack. She grabs their little necks and twists them to attention.

I feel dizzy imagining myself inside out, like a bucket overturning. Shopping bags, birthday presents, Thanksgiving turkeys—these are things you should take the insides out of.

The room is starting to tilt, so I lean into the cupcake box and reach for the exclamation point.

Mom swoops in and delivers a hug from behind. She whispers in my ear. "Our miracle is finally happening. I love you so much."

I wish I had words left, but my mouth feels like limp frosting.

In the car, Mother mostly stares out the driver's side. I throw my feet up in front of me, resting my old shoes on the upholstery. They've been worn soft and I need new ones, but I'll never ask for them.

New car is my mother's favorite smell in the world. I watch her eyes shifting between my shoes and the road: shoes, road, shoes, road. She sinks and settles into her seat.

In many ways, my mother is mystery. I hate when people ask me how Mother is doing because I've never known the answer.

We see the first sign for the airport and Mother suddenly puts a hand out on my leg like we're crashing. I can see she's alarmed at how cold her hands must feel to me. She clears her throat and slowly pulls her fingers back, curling them like a spider's legs when it dies for the last time.

✴

This is what a box is like.

We are in room with the blood sucked out of the walls. Everything is either beige or brown, and there isn't a round object in sight. The clock is a hexagon. I think it's because squares are more man than circles.

Troy, the therapist, is a trim and well-dressed man with thick-rimmed glasses he's hoping will make him interesting. Dark, slick hair frames the cover of his face. When he smiles, too many of his teeth are sharp.

"Thank you for coming, Benjamin. We've heard a lot about you." I think he means more than he's saying. I wonder what Mother has told him. Probably too much.

"Conversion can be a difficult process," he says with his hands laced like a prayer.

I pretend to be surprised. "You mean you can't just flip a switch? That's what I've always been told." My mind is full of proverbs rolling off red lips.

Troy laughs a little too hard. He says I'm a funny guy. "There's no question you'll struggle a bit," he continues, "but many of our staff can attest to the program's success. Myself included." He makes a face like he's thrown open a game show door and is expecting me to be shocked. I'm not.

While Troy sorts out the paperwork, I try to relax. I can hear rumbling outside. Maybe a train, a factory or just the city trying to breathe.

He lays out a few forms for me to sign, explaining the different treatments—voice lessons, physical training and psychiatric sessions. I pick up the pen on the desk and realize I'm afraid. I'm approaching corners and have never felt a collision.

As if on cue, Troy says, "We'll take good care of you." I don't look at his face but I hear his voice. He's oddly comforting. I have always been captivated by the sound of kindness. My roots will latch onto anything.

I dole out my signature on each page, imagining I am drawing pictures. In my name, hidden: the curl of a new sprout, the swing of suspension bridges. But I feel my body stretching. I'm pulling whatever I can inside, shielding myself from the kiss of an unforgiving surface.

*

I'm walking down to the corner store for milk. I can't fathom the idea of dry cereal. Cracks against the roof of a raw mouth.

I've begun to notice how different my walk feels now. In therapy we try to fix both our bodies and our minds. I pretend weights are in my arms to keep them from swinging when I walk. My hands used to make flicking movements in conversation like I was swatting smoke. Now, the sick I wore outside has been prayed away, but the new shell feels fragile.

I am manmade.

Our first group therapy session was an ice cream social where we met for the first time. We wrote our names in fat permanent marker, plastic tags pinned to breast pockets.

I introduced myself to a guy whose nametag read "Lady Steven." His shirt was too tight, so his nametag was on his belt. He made big sweeping gestures like a maestro. Like an expert. I felt small next to him. We were supposed to say what we wanted from all of this. I started to talk about my mother, expecting him to interrupt, but he never did. He just narrowed his eyes and tilted a little, like one side of his head was weighing too much.

I learned that Lady Steven's church had sent him too. But he'd already decided what to be.

"I'm here to prove someone wrong. I swear to you, Benjamin," he said, clicking a painted fingernail to his nametag. "I'm going to keep this."

We live in the same building, but I haven't seen Lady Steven around much. The last time I only heard him. He was in the hallway, passing my room, humming "She'll Be Coming 'Round the Mountain."

In the store, I'm relieved by certainty. Sure enough, I find the milk in its proper section. The eggs are still here. I feel content like someone kept a promise.

In the checkout line, I watch the black-haired girl at the cash register. She is pretty with small features like a doll. I think of Mother's complete set. Because the glass case in her room was full, she kept one of the dolls in my room, above my dresser. She wore all red, with a big feathered hat like a Southern belle. I never saw her face up close because the plastic bag was covered in dust. This girl is close enough.

She rings up my milk carton with her head down. Then I realize she's eyeing at my chest, where a little bit of hair peeks out of the collar. I catch her gaze and send it darting back to an appropriate place. She hides a flash of smile behind her hand. I smile back because I've decided to try something new. I wonder if my teeth are sharp enough.

Behind her, something prints with a buzz. I see the girl writing something down on the bottom of the receipt before she hands me everything in a bag. She winks as I turn to leave. I forget how to respond. We're both trying too hard.

Outside in the street, I dig the receipt out of the bag. She's written a poem for me with just numbers. The digits curl like a lost language. Lost or misplaced.

An image of Troy enters my mind. Tomorrow, behind a pad, his lips will form questions. My mind will scrape together ragged answers, wondering if anyone else in the world has to think this much.

So I try to envision a life with this girl, drawing white away from her face, overflowing for her like a champagne bottle. Then I realize that there are no waves—the ocean is plastic. I've never wanted anything less.

I arrive at my building. In the lobby, the mailbox keyholes are eyes lined up to greet me. I haven't checked my mail all week.

I think about being home. After she found out, Mother used to pray for me in the middle of the night. I'd feel the thick of her hand on my forehead and pretend to be asleep. But I'd also pretend something was changing. Maybe I could will it. The future we both wanted was in there somewhere. A wife to go to church with. I'd bring her to Christmas parties. Grandchildren, for her. My mother tried so hard. She'd grip me by the stem, lifting and cursing an absent man, but I was afraid of open air. I was made to be.

My mother's hand, the pastor's hand, Casey's hand. Everyone's hand was always somewhere else. They were putting faith in something. For them, words came so easily.

I move back to the mailboxes and slip the girl's number into my slot. I hear the soft scrape of landing like a seed. Things grew back home because you looked up and asked nicely. I feel like I should say something for luck, but I never learned how to utter a prayer.

The elevator behind me arrives with a bell. Inside, I hear the shuffle of someone gathering belongings, anxious to get out. Maybe it's the answer I've been waiting for. I stand at the door, trying to look ready, but I don't know what to do with my hands.

NO LESBIANS, CHILDREN OR PETS

DELANEY NOLAN

When I moved into the trailer the clapboard was peeling, the petunias were already dead. Laramie said it was the paradise of Thibodaux. Licked his lips.

The advertisement he placed in the newspaper read: "60 y.o. disabled veteran seeks female roommate. Free rent and board. Send pics." And me, I moved in because my back's shot, the kid's gone, and I couldn't think of a reason not to. Me with my nails split, my roots showing through.

So here I wear fur coats to bed. I don't walk in rented shoes. What would've been the landlord's money bought me crowns; I used to have a dog's teeth, understand? And so not sorry, no regretting. No black crows on my sill watching me wake. There's a needlework circle on the ratty armchair, says, "LOVE THY NEIGHBOR." Yesterday I looked in the mirror and didn't recognize my thighs. My doors don't have locks, but I wouldn't use them anyway. What's a woman have against a human kindness that takes away nothing? I will prove to you: it's just a body.

LESLIE ANNE McILROY MOLLY

Thanks to Chuck Palahniuk's Guts

I keep thinking about the taxidermist,
the one I met at the bar, who scoops
road kill from Route 28 with her apron on,
deplumes the turkey in the trunk of her car
in a lit strip mall at 1 a.m. so as not to disturb
her landlady with an obsession for feathers,
evisceration. She drinks Framboise.

She's not a real redhead, you know, and won't
work for hunters. She salvages, repurposes,
makes necklaces from fox teeth, and to hear
her tell it, that day the contractors pulled
the plug on her freezer was the saddest
day ever—she lost everything, I mean
everything. And her eyes are really big.

She reads stories about boys jacking off
while sitting on the circulation pump
at the bottom of the pool, so bent on
cumming, so holding their breath,
they don't notice their large intestine/s

being sucked down the drain through
their ass/es and have to bite through
the rubber/flesh/hose of their colon/s
and the corn/shit inside them to save
themselves. She recommends the author
highly and you feel yourself shutting up
about metaphor/loss/longing, sick
to your stomach, holding your breath.

And I keep thinking if you were here,
you'd fall in love with her, too, except
you'd want all of her. You'd be sad
when she says she's too busy with
knives/totems/grouses to bother
with a boyfriend, that she loses a part
of herself every time she hooks up.
Her name is Molly/Molly/Molly and I repeat it
like the name of a cocktail/storm/stray—
like the name of the girl that poor boy
was beating off to when his cum came
like pearls in chlorine, when he floated
naked to the top to find his insides out.

MICHAEL MLEKODAY

WITH NEW WAVE BLASTING FROM
THE SPEAKERS, CAPTAIN JOHN
BROWN CONSIDERS TWERKING
AT THE QUEER PARTY

It's just the synth. It's just
the x in vox. It's just the way
syrup feels like my hips'
spirit animal. I'm sure
the sprinklers could open up
like bounding land mines
right now and dancers
would be martyrs to water.
My bones are spring action
toys waiting for that boy's hands,
that girl's fantasy world,
to touch them back to life.
I died once. I was God's wrath
wrapped in flesh and I was
unwrapped at the gallows.
They buried me with the noose
still strung around my neck
like it would raise me up again,
and here, in this basilica
of sweat and liberation,
I'm afraid to let my pink
skinny tie rock to the beat
as my ass, God-sculpted
and alive, pulls me to the fringe

of the dance floor, the femme

who smells like plum

rakes me into the crowd,

and the sprinklers, perfectly-

timed, rain the party

through my skin.

MICHAEL MLEKODAY

CAPTAIN JOHN BROWN STANDS OUTSIDE THE WESTBORO BAPTIST CHURCH HOLDING HIS RIFLE AND BIBLE

We freed Kansas once.
My sons and I prayed
over our blades and bullets
every morning. When you
pray, do your words knife-edge
the hair from your cheeks?
Do you sing and sign
your prayers with blood?
Your own? Marriage is
the easy part: it means promising
yourself to this free soil,
praising sex and death and all
the sweetness and curve
and pulse of the body.
While you blush and sweat
at the thought of a nude
Christ on the cross,
I press my lips to his feet,
his thighs. This is prayer.
We freed Kansas once,
but you came back sticky
as a memory of shame.
I can see you with the only
weapons you know,

dragging a razor through

bible pages, hammering nails

through your own palms

to make sure your wrists

aren't limp.

MICHAEL MLEKODAY

DRAG KING AS CAPTAIN JOHN BROWN

I'm packing tonight.
Weaponry and shipwreck
are the only songs I know.
I grow inches grinding
on this bible, my hair
cut uneven and loosed
like a saliva-laced curse.
The straight men here
see me an armory
waiting to be broken
into, my chest bound,
my skin holding back
some louder dance.
They don't expect
this broadsword, this blood
in my beard. So thick
they have to ask
if it's real.

SOFT

REBECCA HAZELWOOD

Listen. I can almost hear the arrowhead slicing through the paper target, piercing the bale of styrofoam in our front yard. There's a reverb, a sound of wobbling because my nine-year-old arms are too weak for a clean shot. I'd never kill a deer with those arms. Those are the soft arms of a tenderhearted child.

My father tried to teach me how to hunt, to thread the groove of an aluminum arrow onto the bowstring and hold tight. Pull back. Let go. But my blue bow was just too much for me. Too much weight, too much bulk. I couldn't see where the preparation would pay off, when or where it would be necessary to use such brawn. I'd never etch deep muscles in my arms. I'd never leave the yard and take to the woods with my bow. We spent summer evenings tensing and releasing, shooting and retrieving arrows, but my father and I would never hunt in tandem. We would never align his gold bow and my blue one and shoot together. We'd never seek synchronicity in our shooting.

On a day my mother was out of town, my father took me deer hunting. I watched as he scaled the tree to sit in his wooden stand. The higher he was, the farther he was from me. I sat on the hard ground and covered myself in the gold-vermillion leaves, with a chapter book, a text book, some notebook paper, a pencil, and a couple of erasers to keep me busy.

We waited. Restless, I rustled the leaves and he called down, told me to be quiet. He was patient but I was not. To my relief, no deer came near us. I couldn't handle the death of a deer, couldn't watch my father drag its soft brown hide to the truck while its thick blood drained behind us. I couldn't watch an animal suffer.

Sometimes my father hauled home a deer by himself, pulling his truck into the side yard and opening the tailgate so he could climb inside and hold up the head for me to see. The deer's open eyes, glassy and black, stared at me as its remaining cool blood pooled in the crevices of my father's truck bed liner. My father gripped the seven- or eight- or nine-point rack and I snapped a Polaroid. I hated it. But my father told me that he killed bucks because they bullied does. So he became the savior of young deer and I was his documentarian. We were a team.

After, I watched as he backed his truck into the garage and dragged the deer out. He tied a rope around the deer's legs and used his lean, muscled arms to hoist the lifeless body up towards the metal hook on the ceiling. I'd go back inside the house to avoid the entrails on the ground, but I always came back to see my father's hands at work. For hours, he worked with knives and saws to split open the ribs and separate the body into steak, sausage, and organ meat. The heart was the prize. Often, I heard nothing save his sighs and the steady back and forth of the handsaw making a suss-suss sound like a piece of sandpaper in motion.

Sometimes he didn't finish. Sometimes he left half a deer, skinned and stripped of everything but its cold hard side, stuffed into the old garage refrigerator until he could get to it. I could still smell the fresh wild flesh, gamey but mild, lingering in that refrigerator long after he cleaned it out and sanitized it. I can almost smell it now.

My father rarely sent the entire deer to a butcher, preferring the cleanliness of his own hands and the satisfaction of grinding his own sausage. But we always had white, waxy, wrapped packs of deer meat in our freezer, and somewhere in back was a frozen deer heart saved for later.

✳

Listen. The calm and authoritative voices of dispatchers and patrolmen murmured on the police radio as my father drove us out by the distillery, the old plant board, the Prince Hall cemetery, looking for rabbits. The last rays of the bourbon sky set hours before we left the house, hours before the rabbits came out of their holes. My father would shine the headlights of his police cruiser around the edges of vacant brick buildings and headstones, looking for the soft spotted fur of wild, red-eyed rabbits. They couldn't know that we could still see them, hiding their heads but not their bodies.

My father relied on my young eyes to scan the horizon with him. He said my eyes were better than his, stronger and more alert, able to see what he couldn't see. He said I was a better version of him. I knew I had to protect my tender eyes, make them stronger by eating carrots and wearing sunglasses. But no matter how keen-eyed I was, I'd never be able to shoot rabbits like him. Or eat them. I'd never be able to completely separate the wild creatures he shot from the domesticated rabbits we owned.

Was there much difference between those wild rabbits and ours? Sneakers was my favorite, the soft, black-bodied bunny with white paws. We brought him home in my first grade year and overlooked the chewed cords and round droppings behind the couch. When I dressed Sneakers in my frayed baby blue dress and held him while swaying and singing, my father filmed me with a borrowed police station camcorder.

My father said wild rabbits were tougher, smarter than our bunnies, but I wasn't sure until Sneakers and our downy white bunny, Snowball, had babies in the winter. I watched Snowball leave her hairless, wrinkled offspring on the cold metal wire of their outdoor cage where the wind froze them to death. This was despite the warm, lined box we left for

Snowball and Sneakers. My father said that rabbits survived in the wild and multiplied, but bunnies didn't. I understood the difference, but couldn't stomach the sight of lean pink rabbit legs and torsos in our refrigerator.

But was there really much difference between Sneakers and the fat neighborhood cat that dug up my mother's tulips? My father said the fat cat did too much damage, so he stalked the cat from the shadows of our front porch. He taught me how to pump the cold metal lever of his pellet gun and wait. When the cat pranced into the rays of our sodium streetlight, my father put pellets no bigger than chocolate chips into the cat's butt. He never asked me to shoot the gun. I'd never be able to keep a steady hand, never be able to teach the cat a lesson. But I trusted my father's motive was to instruct rather than kill the cat.

✳

Listen. I can almost hear the Walther 380 firing in my hands, hitting the tin can on a hill of Granny Rose's farm. Almost. I can almost hear the trees shaking gently like beans in a maraca, feel the cool gray air of the sky, see the abandoned chicken coops and filmy pond surrounding us. Almost. My ears were stuffed with two white buds, the butt end of cigarettes my father carved in two when he forgot earplugs. He said I must protect my hearing when discharging a gun; the cotton filters would muffle the sound, soften but not erase the ringing in my ears.

My father taught me to hold steady and line the steel sights with the tin can. He said I might be knocked back, but my arms couldn't really know the force of the bullets hitting the tin, the way the gun would kick me back a step. Such a small, hard object in my hands. Such soft arms. After I fired the gun, my father said I had good aim, near perfect, like I was made to shoot a gun or maybe made to be his daughter. "Is there anything you can't do, kid?" he asked. We kept shooting, denting the tin can and riddling it with bullet holes by the time we finished.

In my young hands, I could hold a small handgun or lighter bow, but my father kept the big guns to himself. He used a muzzleloader I never saw and a wooden shotgun I don't remember shooting. I could never load the blackpowder. I could never cock open a shotgun and push in the blue plastic shells, knowing their pellets would shatter to pieces inside a soft animal body. Shooting those guns was my father's activity; picking up the shells was mine. My father knew I'd never survive the killing.

He never asked me to prepare as he did, to lather up with green scentless hunting soap, to wash the human off me. He never bought me heavy cotton coats with fleece lining, or one-piece padded camouflage suits to withstand the cold. He never gave me sharp knives or handsaws to carve up deer carcasses. He knew my arms were too soft to carve the flesh, my heart too weak to pull the trigger or make an animal into meat.

Still, I wanted to crawl inside my father's skin, to make myself as much in his image as possible. If my father never bought me hunting gear, I wanted to wear it anyway. For Halloween one year, I put my legs into his one-piece padded camo suit and tucked myself inside, slowly zipping the shell over my body. On a night haunted by princesses and witches, I made myself the proud daughter of a hunter.

THE GEOGRAPHY OF SQUARES AND CIRCLES

JOSEPH DANTE

1.

y family is the seasons.

Mom raises the windows and invites the light to stay. She goes to sleep when you expect her to and winds herself up again, every day, like a twinkling music box. Her ears are so used to the bells. When they ring, she pops up with flowers or gardens of food. If you let her in, color will breathe into your dank apartment. Nothing is a cave.

Dad makes everything hot with his collection of red sauces, laying them out on the table like a chemistry set. He will have lost all his taste soon enough and will only be eating the texture his tongue rubs up against. He burns up at every screen he sees, demanding everything be free as holiday. There is little that escapes him, very little that doesn't end up bubbling.

Leanna dances on all kinds of stages, moving from soft to strict, carrying her steps to whispers or slingshot crescendos that give her flight. She's always on her toes and drags us everywhere she thinks we need to go. When not acting her part as a spirit with muscles attached, she's rescuing her heart from a hero. A hero that will inevitably trip out of her room, later remain nameless. She's a pearly figurine, and pearls have always been her thing.

Me, I cover myself completely. Heavy coats and wild hair like fur out of a burrow. I'm long in the arms and fair in the face and I've always been afraid of coming apart. I prefer the dark.

2.

Sitting at the perfectly square table, my family is a compass with a broken needle. Mom talks about the way she moves too fast at her job, making everyone else look bad and getting a scolding from her supervisor. The bigger the hair, the bigger the trouble, she says. Dad talks about blowing leaves on the neighbors' lawn because of the yippy dog and midnight fiestas. I look out the window for a sense of direction or to relearn prayer, I'm not sure. Maybe an arrow will show up in the flocks. I am supposed to be a westward representative at this daily orientation, but I always feel like I'm heading south. South is where I wouldn't be able to

stare at windows, south is down and inside. When my eyes
don't return, Mom shuts the blinds and keeps talking. Leanna
takes out nail polish remover and dabs it on cotton balls. It
stinks up the kitchen like gossip. Without looking anywhere
else, she applies a new coat of polish, the kind that cracks
like her joints, like her laugh, before Dad sits down with the
brownest pear he can find.

3 .

My family is the four corners of a map.

Mom is an island and puts all the trash out to sea. Papa's
cancer that drags out painfully like American romantic
comedies, the idea of breaking off the last branches, her son's
fog that she can see from her highest canopy. Nothing will
happen, she knows and she waves.

Dad is a metropolis and knocks on all the doors. You get the
news quick, no postage needed. There will be signs, fireworks,
commercials, movies. ECONOMY! ALMOND MILK IN
WATERFALLS! EXCHANGES FOR EXCHANGES! There
will be no cubicles and only robots will lift the boxes.

Leanna is an archipelago with little space between the pieces.
Secretary for Key Club, Seat Closest to Mr. Lucas Lionnel,
Dancer with the Biggest Bag and the Smallest Circle of Friends.
She sprays herself with Sensual Amber, wondering how amber
can be sensual in the first place because it's amber. She keeps

lavender notebooks to fit herself together
because she's most afraid of letting herself
scatter.

I've never written anything about our shapes
except this. I'm not going to say if I'm the
tundra on this map or the aurora above.
Drifting or shifting, it doesn't matter, but
the only shape to this unit that seems to
have invisible movements. Mom is mistaken
and cannot see far from her trees. Dad
has light pollution to deal with and all the
explosions. Leanna only knows a single kind of
temperature. I don't blame them for stretching
themselves across so much water. I blame
myself for becoming obsessed with measuring
distances. My cartography is always atomic.

4 .

My family is either a wheel or a wreath. It's
hard to tell, it's an optical illusion. When I do
come apart and break open in the tub, Mom
shoots up from the couch like it's just on
time. Alarms, bells, sunlight—all at once. Dad
smashes a glass when he makes the discovery
and his blood mingles with mine. I watch the
ribbons closely, as hard as I can to keep my eyes

open, while Leanna runs down the stairs. Mom reports how my sister did the rescuing this time, so poised on the phone, no crying. The turning begins when they've seen me as something else: Mom is a muted autumn, Leanna can see the fog that has wrapped around me, Dad is the fixed North. It's a wheel. I have never been naked for so long at once and I finally see how white I've gotten. My family stands around the bed and they're all holding shapes I don't recognize. It's a wreath. But they fall away so fast I don't have to interpret or measure them anymore. The color Mom brings is going too. Pink, peach; beige, sawdust. Everything is a cave.

GREGORY SOLANO

FOR DIEGO, DRINKING ALONE

Diego, no one is there but you
to remember that summer we spent
between your home in that broken down
school bus in Little Haiti and my bed,
sleeping side by side every night
like impoverished brothers. No one knows
how I cleaned the sheets every
Monday morning to wash away
the stench of animals that you pressed
into them, how in Kentucky you
washed your clothes in a river
that could never make them clean.
By then I was in New York and you
whispered to me from a wired telephone
in a farmer's library. The shrieking of bats
as you'd reach into the farthest shelves.
On the lower east side I kept a bed
with a girl who hated poetry. And so
it was to you that I read from that
small, humiliating room five stories
above the ground. Just as there was no one but you
to watch the cow go down with milk fever,
to band the goats, to feed the rooster,
to break the necks of the chickens

and deplume them. The Walkman

on your hip replaying Steiner's lectures

on the creation of souls almost silently

as you moved across the crumbling barn.

Though now you drink on the far coast,

alone and in secret, it's because you are a stranger

most of all to yourself. Alone with ourselves

just as we were then, turning over.

LOA, UTAH: 1945

AMASA GUY

I.

Dan Ramage and his grandson Guy lived on a farm three miles from town with no auto, no electricity, no plumbing, and no woman. Guy was seven. Dan was sixty.

The little boy walked to town alone each week, three miles from Grandpa Dan's farm to Grandma Effie's house, along a gravel road that passed by nothing but sage brush, jack rabbits, the abandoned dump. He threw rocks at the rabbits. He was tempted by the dump.

He bathed behind the stove in Grandma's kitchen. He donned clean clothes for the only time that week. He went to the movie, walking two blocks up and back, along dirt streets boarded by overhanging trees watered by the irrigation ditch. It was a beautiful walk on a big-moon night.

He slept alone in Grandma's middle room under quilts that weighed him into sleep. At eight-thousand feet, night air was frosted, even in the house, even in July. He rose on Sunday, pleased if he hadn't peed in bed, crushed if he had, if the women said something. Barefoot, he walked across a gravely yard to the three-hole privy out back by the pig-pen.

He listened to the zing, zing of Ruffus Tanner milking cows at dawn.

He ate breakfast at Grandma's table, a banquet of food, fresh cow's milk, slabs of Wilma's bread, fried eggs, pan-meat, oatmeal, jam, pie and bottled apricots, coffee for the women. Then, when the tower-bell rang a second time, he walked to church and sat in the horse-shoe balcony and stared at the unplayed organ thinking it anciently old.

After lunch, he returned three miles to the farm alone, anxious to see Dry Valley loom below as he reached the edge of the bluff, which he climbed down by the cut-off that Grandpa built with his team. At the farm, he was smothered by kisses from the dog. Grandpa said, "She won't eat while you are gone." That night he slept in the iron bed with Grandpa and Shadow among the turkeys.

The next night they sat on the old man's stoop in silence, surrounded by silence except for frogs and the old man's voice spinning tales while he smoked and watched the neighbor's light a mile away. Dan told of Sonny, his worthless son-in-law from Oklahoma who claimed that he could make the Model A pump water to Dan's turkey flock. It never happened. He never fixed the Model A, nor rigged the pump. Some mechanic! Sonny would always be a footloose redneck dreamer who produced smart kids; stunning daughters and handsome sons, who did well, married well, and lived in comfort.

Dan told of the day a young man came to collect for hauling feed. Dan couldn't pay. The young man raised his voice. Dan's dog growled and made a feint toward the younger man, who said, "I've a 30-30 rifle in my truck." Dan said, "What makes you think you'll make it to your truck? My 300 Savage stands behind this door." All silence as they measured one another. The young man saw the old man's eyes and decided that the odds were high. He retreated, glaring.

Dan spoke of Doan Morrell, his wife's bastard son, for whom the old man banked deep anger. They were partners once in trucking; the venture failed. Dan held the debt. Effie stood for Doan against Dan's anger, which she knew was aimed at her and the lover in her need, Hiette Morrell, Doan's father. She left the farm to live in town, angry words left unhealed.

Dan was lonely. He told how things would be next summer. Guy would return. They would break the colt. The boy would learn to ride. They would camp and fish on Thousand Lake. It never happened.

11.

Dan Ramage lived lonely in a one-room shack on a rocky farm in Dry Valley. I never saw him sleep in Grandma's house in town. I never saw her on the farm. No divorce. He came when daughters came. Grandpa sat by the kitchen stove with his hat on his shoes off, his wool-socked feet stuffed in the oven,

Bull Durham in one hand, coffee in the other, happy, holding court. The feud backed off a bit when the girls were there. But I never saw him stay after others went to bed. He rode bareback, three miles north to the hut where he slept cold with his dog.

Dan didn't like old-age lonely. Neither did she; they were stubborn. Dan hated alms. He wanted no help from wealthy in-laws. Ramage was as good as any Stewart. He refused a house owned by his wife, bought with Stewart money.

She would not return to the farm. Effie was tired of a crude cabin with no lights, no water, no place to relieve herself, except behind tall sage. She was tired of doing laundry on a scrub-board, tired of walking three miles to town, three back, over which in days past, she carried a baby in one arm and led a toddler by the hand. Effie wanted neighbors: Tanner to the North, Sorensen on the northeast corner, the Pierce place to the south. She wanted Relief Society during the week, Sunday school in the morning, sacrament meeting at night. She wanted a store close by, a movie on the weekend, a locker at the ice plant for her meat. She needed a few decencies, and with failing health, she wanted a break from the drudgery of living on a primitive, isolated farm.

Dan reminded Effie that she begged him to leave the mines, that she promised to endure any ill so long as he would quit those frightful death traps and come home each night.

They loved each other.

He kept his word. He worked himself close to death to force a living out of rock and alkali. He labored as a father to Will Covington's two girls, to Hiette Morrell's bastard son, to his own six children. And not a living son to ease the load.

Now she was backing off because the Stewarts gave a house with lights and running water, implying that all he gave was not enough; he wasn't up to par. He stood his ground, at the farm. She stood her ground, in town.

Dan saw winter coming. He could not stand another long cold spell alone. He sold the farm and cows, two horses and the shack, went on the road with his dog, hopped the mail to Salina, rode north on the Greyhound bus, stayed with daughters a month or two at every stop.

Dan was killed in Price, working construction. He fell from the running board and was crushed beneath the wheels of a heavy-loaded truck. Dan's body lay all day and night in the living room of the house that Stewarts gave to Effie. He was buried in the graveyard given by Stewarts to the town.

PLANCHE, WHIP, SALTO

BECKY ADNOT-HAYNES

I.

ou spotted the trapeze rig in the spring, where it seemed to have sprouted, like a flower, from its otherwise concrete surroundings. It was pitched on a medium-sized plot of grass in what counts as a park in your Midwestern city, and you passed it as you drove across town to go to the new international food market to buy ingredients for a complicated Asian noodle dish. You are at an age—thirty one—at which you suddenly aspire to be thought of as a foodie.

It was empty, that day: There were no other hints of circus around—no jugglers, no fire-eaters, no high-wire act—and the trapeze looked lonesome there all by itself, nobody swinging into its net, nobody sitting in the half-ring of bleachers that surrounded it. You didn't think about it as you and your husband ate dinner that night, your noodles fragrant with Thai basil and delicious, a rare success (except for two varieties of grilled cheese sandwich, which you do very well, you are not a good cook). But the next week when you drove by, this time with the goal of homemade sushi, there were figures swinging delicately to and fro from the contraption, and you nearly rear-

ended the Toyota in front of you. You found the trapeze school on the internet, where you learned that they give performances on Friday nights and lessons on Saturdays. *Experience the thrill of the flying trapeze! All levels welcome!* And so that Friday you dragged your husband to the spot, half-expecting the whole thing to have vanished, like a mirage. But there it was, beautiful at night in the glow of white lights. You took note of the fact that the bleachers were half-empty in only a peripheral way, watching in awe as the aerialists tossed their lithe bodies from bar to bar. "It was okay, I guess," said your husband, who has very specific preferences—romantic comedies with unhappy endings, partially-finished basements, steak only if he doesn't have to see it raw first— and then the two of you went out for pizza. But the next afternoon you tied your hair into a ponytail and fished out a pair of old spandex shorts and went bravely back, determined to try this thing for yourself.

II.

You didn't know that it would feel a little bit like sex—the bodily connection, the fitting together of parts—the small *oh!* you released when Isaac, the lead aerialist, caught you by the forearms and held you swinging through the air, an incredible three or four seconds of weightlessness until he dropped you gently to the net. You didn't know that when the sweet, fresh-faced college student behind you in the fly order, also taking her very first lesson, cried *thank you!* and *that was wonderful!* as she landed on the net after being caught by Isaac that you would know exactly how she felt (amazed, grateful). You didn't know that when Isaac, halfway up the ladder, turned back and said to you *I want to catch you again* that it would feel like your heart leaving your chest.

He is so beautiful you almost cannot believe it. As a girl you were used to boys who were sweaty and awkward, who you developed crushes on despite their tendency to talk too loud and too quickly, despite their outfits picked out so obviously by their mothers. They were boys whose over-long limbs seemed not a part of them; boys who touched you with clumsy sweaty fingers and then waited eagerly for their turn. At some point these boys became men who worked in marketing and knew a lot about microbrews and played kickball on weeknights, who took you out to respectably nice restaurants before touching you with clumsy sweaty fingers and then waiting, only slightly less eager, for their turn. With his black eyes and dark curly hair, Isaac is beautiful in a nearly Biblical way: You think that he would not have looked out of place in the Garden of Eden, a banana leaf over his crotch.

You didn't know that you'd be back the next Saturday, and the next Saturday after that. You didn't know that you'd fake severe menstrual cramps to get out of a trip to the vineyards with friends two Saturdays later. You didn't know that you'd

take such pure and unsullied pleasure in leaping from a board two stories above ground, in learning how to get upside down, how to arch your back to look for the catch. You even like the terminology that the aerialists use, even before it makes any sense to you, those beautiful strange words: *planche, whip, salto.* Every action of your adult life is a measured, careful decision, even things that are supposed to be fun—what kind of frozen yogurt to buy, whether to go to the movies or rent one at home—and you take an uncomplicated joy in your uncomplicated accomplishments on the trapeze. *Joy* is not a word you can use to describe any other singular thing in your life. You work for a company that assesses the competency of call center agents—which agents do a good job solving customer problems, which do a poor job, and which do very subtle gradations of jobs in between. None of you, except a plumpish, forty-something women who always declines your invitations to go for drinks, care anything whatsoever for your jobs.

You didn't know that when you didn't tell your husband how much you love the trapeze that this would feel like a small betrayal, and you didn't know that you'd fall in love with Isaac the way you fell in love with Mike

DeCarmo sophomore year of high school—recklessly, carelessly, with the hot spark of adolescence. You didn't know flying the trapeze would make you realize things about your marriage, like how you wished your husband danced at weddings, how you hated that he suspected a conspiracy in everything—even the price of ice-cream cones—how when you're with him you turn into a sly, sneering version of yourself. You didn't know that on the eve of your thirty-second birthday, one month after your first trapeze lesson, you would realize that you didn't want children, despite the plan you and your husband meticulously plotted out, the first pregnancy at thirty three and the second at thirty five, the (admittedly small) college savings already socked away. You didn't know that when you told your husband this that he would say *that's okay* and then take a pair of pruning shears to the bushes around your house until they looked small and sad and eventually one of them sort of shriveled up and died. You didn't mean for that to happen.

III.

You didn't know that Isaac would like you back. That he'd notice as your old gymnastics training came back to you, the muscle memory returning slowly, from wherever it was stored away (forever, you thought) and push you to learn harder and harder tricks on the trapeze, back-end straddle whips and penny rolls and then layouts and double-backs, performing catches with you himself (always), lifting you by your hands your ankles your waist, the two of you a perfect match with your strong lean bodies and dark hair, like brother and sister, almost, except that the parts of your body he touches pulse white-hot for days, until

finally the part of you he touches is your lips, and you think you might die, immediately and without warning, from happiness.

But you don't die. You keep flying, every Saturday, except now Isaac meets you some weeknights, too, at the company's indoor rig. You do catch after catch, his hands wrapped firmly around your wrists, and when you finally sleep with him (quietly and urgently, on the trapeze net) it doesn't occur to you that this is a worse transgression than what you have already done.

You didn't know that when the owner of the trapeze company offered you a job that you would accept, that you'd leave your job, your 5 percent 401k match, your fourteen paid vacation days per year, to make thirteen-fifty an hour as a junior-level aerialist at a trapeze school, that in the third decade of your life you'd start anew, having discovered pieces of you that you didn't know existed, sparks and flashes of something presumed long dead. When you tell your husband about your decision he registers the shock quietly, mostly in his eyebrows, and does not challenge you.

On the night of your very first performance, you change into your leotard in a trailer dashed away on the edge of the patch of grass and do your own hair and makeup with the other female aerialists. When you gaze at yourself in the mirror, at your hair pulled back tightly and your eyes dark with mascara, you think that you have never looked so beautiful, not even on your wedding day. Isaac has slicked his dark hair back and when his face appears behind yours in the mirror your breath catches in your throat at his loveliness.

You didn't know that on the night of your first performance you'd look out into the crowd, glittering sparsely with cameras, and see your husband's face. You didn't know that you'd be able to hold his gaze as you climbed up to the platform, hands chalked, ready for Isaac, who waits for you on the other side, and think only of the uprise forward-over you are about to perform. You didn't know that you were the kind of person who would let go of something, but you are swinging now, and there is Isaac, ready to catch you if you are ready to reach toward him, to let his hands grasp your forearms. You didn't know this, but there it is, and there you are.

From obelisk stamen, locus of spore, a magenta irradiate. Chroma is how colour breathes. Erected apart, a colonnade. Apple trees apple trees apple trees. For every lintel of leaves a fall of adams. Begin with water and fathom tensile strength. Because a glass, and a glass of, is the difference between: wet, hard. Or when it means to break or when it means to permeate. Body should and will collapse you to pure surface (e.g. obsidian, driftglass, chrome). To not fall but for walls, which make a room. Re: verse, in turning, a third may also make a word for it is room. Inside the house, a glass house. Inside, every room must measure from left to right a phalanx of torsos. Shadow is how corners breathe. To inhale, light. When and in flood as though of an end had wood drunk, distends. That is, an imbibition. Contracts (a mad July, weather-withered) on desiccation. When a line swells we can say it is vexed. When crossed, intersected. It is up to walls to settle the point where one becomes a crux of two or worse, three, each clean cleave. Graphs ensure that in spite of what two planes of colour might close off, your north and south darken a true entrance. There is not to be a door. There are never to be any doors and only an arc ending one or any other transaction. Ours is too large a distance to measure with anything smaller. To translate: Structure is skeletal, beam femur, load bearing vertebra. Your mouth is how my body breathes. For where the belly caves, we build an apse. This is always underground and facing the orient. That is hers, and his, of course, is cantilever. Forged to outbrute monsoons. At equidistant windows, the eye must first be pleased and so the ocean will end where your eyelashes begin.

PAULA MENDOZA

SHE TELLS THE HILT OF IT

Understand: *I am no small happening*

. . .

More than maddened blood.
Who comes from, becoming more
than what wants—*no small*
miracle, more hue than—inviolate
chroma—my budded pulse.

And I'm more than my soon I so loudly undo yes
I'm much   more.

Sub- and Super-

stratum—under*stood*? More-over, you dig?
Sedi*mental*, mother-....

And more than wielded: Thrice struck. Forged.
Folded in three then three then three again

begin   begin   begin

Word is skinned. Edged sense scintillates
a surface, irised. Prism, or fractal, smallest

mirror—a piece of a piece of.

Farther than hilt, hue, stroke. *More than maddened blood.*
Clay receives, red gives *to the hilt.* Suc-
cumb. I take you like clay. Im-
pressed. Bodied forth. Do I
demean myself? Very well, I demean myself
I contain, I hold in
hand *exergue* worn smooth. An other, jagged.
Flint of obsidian my fingers fret, is a word.
Rune, resin smooth or amber heavy, warm, is a word.
Meaning will blur or wink or cut or
shine, where you licked. Sheeny meridian, to con-
note is fracture, or *flaw.*
Aft to fore-tells its trans-form-ations:

feather, cleavage, knot

What be-comes after so much hard dirt grinding.
Vein of ore but *more than maddened blood, much more.*

       Dirt, then dirt beneath dirt, then sweet
water, underneath. *Under*stand, man?
Loose in the hilts, or haft. Of an iris, otherwise

ensate, so leaves or blade down the gullet. More?
Other haft in hand. More than

this ire is more than desire is more than desirous is more than this is

     more than this—you know—

       there is nothing—

. . .

Understand?   I am no small happening.

The way you silence I am almost conceived. Hard interval's a yarn not even angels believe, what with their not-dying, their not-knowing-how-to-die. Every new hack at the neck flowers another head with hearts for brains. I grow concerned with small things because I will always be a small thing. This doesn't concern *you*. This doesn't *concern* you. Meanwhile everyone's trying to read this book like they're trying to fuck the pretty new girl in school. No one can get past the first sentence. Does it mean *this?* How about *this?* So maybe *this?* The way you read, I am almost December. Remembrance of sleet pricks all my hairs on end. You live in cold and so you will. The way you love me I am almost relieved. After all my ciphering, I am ready to be SEE JANE RUN. Every cut just heals over prettier pearl. I want you to go away or make yourself more mine. It is as simple as nothing is. The way I can't remember how you kiss makes me almost certain almost certain's the most beautiful negation. I am good without him saying so, but some days it's such a terrible effort to know. Meanwhile, I want to be the pretty new girl in school but I don't want to fuck any of you. The way you bore me is almost a pill. I took it with dinner. I took it bent over the counter, my cheek against the faucet. The way I love you, you should be grateful, and very, very afraid.

PAULA MENDOZA

THIS IS THE LAST POEM I'LL WRITE ABOUT YOU III

Narcissus is the wrong
story. Still, where farther inward else
but self? Problem's letting go
the swoon of my fret for you, its gooey
goodness. I guess we sicken
eventually. Inevitably? I guess I'm sick
of the nothing I keep rising above water
to breathe in, and. Well. Nothing.

It's easier to be sucked in
by groundswell. It's easier to spend
a weekend fucked to sore and jelly-kneed
with no heart to stand a head on.
I could go on, and have, and probably
will, lacking it. Heteronomous. I lack
faith, too, in mastery—that eye-gouging
illusion, studded with turrets, towers, sky-
scrapers, complete penile control, and
something about lasers, or sabers, or knives.
Anatomically correct ego's a lie, is grossly
misproportioned, see? Her eyes are too
big, and her yes, too.

But where farther forward than you?
So I keep saying yes, and I say *pour*
and I say *shine*, and *honey*, and *again*
I say many words because I like
rubbing them to a pilled velveteen knap.
I like to rub and rub and rub
the words to softnesses.

Maybe I am making up for your corners?
Maybe I am making up the reason
for this habit? Which you may have
become, among other things: a colour,
a tyrant, a figment, a catalyst.

AT DOLCE VITA ON THE OCCASION OF HER READING BEING INTERRUPTED

PAULA MENDOZA

And even when she is

reacting, naturally

to the words before her, has ever been

otherly

conscious of the performance

of her reacting, to anything (is only one

among many who live lives gazed on) so senses

a stir of some muster at the blur beyond

her shoulder, a young

man approaches, says:

I couldn't help but notice

how engrossed you are

by this book, if you don't mind me

asking, what is it about?

This book is metabolizing its slow

devastation inside her, she is vertiginous

moved to a sweetish nausea, luxuriating

in the narcotic heat

of *poetry!*

but collects herself enough to answer:

It's about the girl made meat.

It's about the slaughter of cows.
And it's about fucking. And mothers
and disease. And language.
And shit.

And love.

And the friendly smile
freezes on his face. And she
is sloe-eyed, soft-lipped
and emptied to him. She is too
impatient
to be amused for very long by
the contortion of his mouth and eyes, his
skin, suddenly
jaundiced, pale
as yellow snow.

PAULA MENDOZA

THE LAST POEM I'LL EVER WRITE ABOUT YOU I

Eyes can hardly recollect, they dilate so

saucerly, I'm moon gone on thinking over it, I'm over it.

I'm not.

I am—*not.*

What classifies a poor excuse?

Of what little use this thing we name a heart.

It has been you before you knew

we have no future together

No sad alternate this graceless fact: I want you

back, or here, or over there

on the shelf, next to the jar pickling my tongue.

Had I nevergreened undone, armored to naked in seconds flat

at the dead blue look of you. Believe me, my love

is true. Or anyway, that's what the humans say

when they have nothing left.

CONSTRUCTING MEANS AND SUMS

MATTHEW ANKENY

SuperBill on table say: $339,234. W/ interest, thirty year: $703,332. Monthly payment: $2,038. Wife on couch, read book. Today, one-third million dollar. Thirty year, three-quarter million dollar. House on Prosper big moneysuck. Sit there on market w/ promise, $100K under value. Real-estate say, Excellent price for fixer-upper. So we buy, add on construction loan. Well on path to American dream, real-estate say. Path to my early grave. Pay $1,650/month for one bedroom rental on Bertona. Rent/mortgage alone: $3,638/month. Jumbo loan still approve, even though Wife no work while on personal pregnancy leave.

I sleep on couch. Wife (w/ pea-in-pod) and toddler (Son) sleep in bedroom. Kid three-year old, take up half bed. Couch no too bad—quiet in AM when wake up, can get coffee w/o wake up Son or Wife. Early in AM go Norcross Way as sun rise slow over horizon. Puget Sound still and quiet, cloud big gray wool blanket. World no awake, feel very much like peace.

Norcross good client, lawyer w/ taste/sensibility, no crown every corner, no wainscoting every wall. Client buy postwar house, add second story, full remodel first floor, new deck in backyard. Make American dream true. Two kid, each w/ own bedroom, plus master bedroom for lawyer and wife w/ walk-in closet. Also master bath w/ shower and tub. Also office downstair, between living room w/ fireplace and family room w/ flatscreen television. Norcross good job, make $60K off $300K remodel, easy money, American saying. I pay down payment for house on Prosper with job profit. Be foreman contractor fifteen year, but best life still to come, as saying go. American dream hang on horizon, can see if meditate long enough.

Former client call while drive Norcross. He want build mother-in-law apartment for Rico. $75K addition to back of Craftsman house. Make $15K if finish job. Concrete already lay, foundation settle. Framer stop show up, so need foreman contractor ASAP, American saying. Right now, Rico drive family up wall. Rico poodle run rampant round Craftsman. Rico sleep in kid bedroom. Two kid sleep in same room, first time in life, fight day and night. No can work for long, family need space to live. Need job quick. He say, So, like, what do you think? How quickly can it be done?

Have job on Norcross, say. Need do siding and finish work. Take two month on weekend finish Rico mother-in-law.

Good enough, son say. When can you drive by?

I drive by now. Turn car, go 31st before go Norcross.

Rico sixty-seven year old. Wear robe, have tattoo on four finger: R-I-C-O. Six year ago, Rico just Richard White. Back then, I do extension on Craftsman for son. Add 400 square feet, kitchen remodel w/ new living room. Put hardwoods on first floor of Craftsman, new kitchen w/ stone countertop, stainless appliance and espresso maker. When wife die, Rico decide it time for three-quarter life crisis. Now stand by Impala, spray paint green w/ sparkle.

We need a nest for Rico, son say.

Un nido para mi, Rico say and smile gold teeth w/ diamond. Skin sag round face, make Rico look sad. Gold teeth like tired attempt at beauty. Rico hold poodle on pink leash. Feet w/ slippers, stand on gravel driveway, look toward foundation. Saw horse set on foundation, plywood spread between, plan spread on plywood. Beautiful white plan by New York City designer, for house here in Magnolia.

Rico say, I wanna feel like it's la ciudad, man.

You are in the city, Dad, son say.

Nah, this is pinche suburbia.

Some people never happy. It city limit. Magnolia good neighborhood for family. Nice place to live, easy place find American dream. Rental on Bertona in Magnolia, and house on Prosper in Magnolia, on top of hill by water tower. Water tower fenced w/ chain link and barbed wire, some teenage graffiti, and little dirt patch w/ grass that die no too long ago. Still nice place to live. Best water pressure in city, real-estate say.

Plan for Rico look simple. Studio apartment. Can work on weekend. Friday-Sunday.

Son say, Whatever it takes to get Rico out of my house.

Rico smile. I'm not all bad, man. Poodle squats to poop. Poop lay on gravel driveway; Rico walk to house. I'm like a talisman or something, Rico say. Good luck to la casa.

Month go by. SuperBill say: $337,645. Everyday, when home from work, walk dog round neighborhood. At night dog sleep on floor by couch. Have one kid, one pea-in-pod, and one dog. Rent one bedroom house. Have house on Prosper, too, buy for $100K under market value. Jumbo loan find American dream. Can build dream w/ four bedroom, living room, kitchen w/ stone counter, stainless appliance, espresso maker. Under $150K to rebuild. Tear down fixer-upper, build new house on land. Labor free because come from me, foreman contractor. Plan is work on house on weekend, rebuild house, move family in big house on top of hill in Magnolia. But plan no work, no yet, because at 31st on weekend for two month. When walk dog round neighborhood, look at house w/ light on, look like snow globe or fish tank lit from inside. Is February and have wonder how warm house feel. Heater at Bertona rental only work some day and no many night. Window leaky w/ air that rush like glass invisible.

One day, while walk dog, see three kid play baseball on dirt area beside water tower. Throw ball, swing, big hit, ball fly over street, hit window on Prosper. Window shatter. Three boy run other way. Dog bark. I walk to house, window on house broken. Open door, dog grab baseball, love chew leather. Glass on floor cut dog paw. Rain that night. Next day, dog limping. Glass inside dog paw, cost $613 for veterinary remove glass from paw. Wife say necessary expense, because dog bring joy to house. Dog big moneysuck. Broken window on house let in rain, warp flooring. Flooring be remove anyway, soon as Rico addition done. Put plywood over window, house look like sad shantytown.

When at Rico on Friday, lawyer client want to know why I no come. I say house almost done. Ahead of schedule, three week, house be done. Want to see house finish right now. Want to move family in because hate live in condominium w/ family. Lawyer have both condominium and house in same city. Condominium in Fremont neighborhood w/ lot of good restaurant, including one I take Wife for first date. Lawyer client say that Fremont condominium big moneysuck when can't rent. He need house to be finish. I be there Friday when appliance come, say.

At night when go to bed, tell Son he need to be lawyer, own both house and condominium. Need do school and learn law of American dream, reach American dream. Son drool on pillow, already sleep. Wife read book to pea-in-pod. She roll eye, keep read. I go to couch and fall sleep right when head hit pillow w/

clothes still on. Wake in big sweat like have bad dream, but don't have dream anymore. When sleep only see black. Then wake, while sun rise slow and turn black into gray. Sky cloudy like big blanket, everyday. When get up, step on dog. Dog whimper, limp to corner, paw wrap in gauze from veterinary that turn white to brown in one day.

On Friday, I at Norcross when appliance arrive for lawyer client. Get big Subzero fridge, stainless steel w/ ice maker inside that make ice cube for you. Also espresso maker, for install in cabinetry on countertop. Espresso maker $599. Same price as fix dog, after tax. Get phone call from Rico, ask why don't show up today.

Tell Rico, Appliance come today for Norcross job, I here for delivery.

Rico no accept. Say need place finish so can rest head, because kid drive Rico up wall. Say, Yeah man, can't even smoke weed in the house, de verdad. Anything you can do? I need this, man.

No worry, I say. I be there tomorrow morning, eight AM.

Can't come earlier? Rico say.

No noise in early AM, I say. On weekend, eight AM first noise.

Rico say, These kids cry at all times of the day, I swear, these things are driving me nuts. Rico mortgage man in former life. Turn into banker for marry wife, wife family own mortgage bank. Rico make lot of money, achieve American dream, wife die, then Rico go crazy. Son now take care of Rico, build mother-in-law to keep close eye.

I be there six AM, real quiet, say. Do electrical wiring, no power tool need.

Great man. Just don't wake los niños.

Real quiet, say. Won't know I there.

I wake five-thirty AM w/o help of alarm. American saying: Early bird get worm. No need alarm because wake five-thirty AM when no feel nose on face. Window like glass invisible, nose feel like icicle in snowstorm. When no can sleep, get up like early bird.

Saturday AM go Rico house, start electric wiring. Rico come in with coffee, seven-thirty AM. Poodle have pink leash with diamond stud collar. Rico wear silk kimono. Rico make small talk. Ask where from. Ask how long work in construction. Ask about family, if have kid, have wife. Small talk on Saturday morning very casual thing for American upperclass. Ask about wiring, what work I do. Ask what food I like eat. Ask I ever miss home. Ask how I like here, in Rico country. Ask if have kid, again. Ask if have wife, again. Ask if hard to become citizen. Ask if I citizen. Ask how I get papers. Is very hard to work while American upperclass small talk. Ask if it hard find work. Ask if I own house. Ask where house is. Rico very surprise, then Rico face change expression. Ask if by water tower. Ask if ever have break in. Ask if that safe part of Magnolia to raise kid. Ask if house old. Ask if have old copper pipe. He nod, like

Rico wise man. Ask if I move to better part of neighborhood when can. Work no get done. Rico lean against counter, cross leg, let go of poodle. Poodle walk over to pile of sawdust, lift leg, pee. Ask why I move country. Ask if family still in country. Ask if Rico country better place. Ask why I no go back. Ask what it take to go back. Ask if I pay tax. Rico nod, no believe. Ask if have kid, again. Ask how old kid. Ask if he go school. Ask if he go college, someday. Ask if hard to keep three-year-old kid off street. Shake head, Tough world out there, Rico say. Mind if I smoke? Rico ask and pull out pipe. Ask if I smoke. Ask if I drink. Laugh, shake head, no believe. Ask I have wife, again. Ask if wife drink. Ask how long be marry. Ask if wife work. Ask if I make good money. Ask if hard find work, again. Ask if I licensed. Work no get done. Morning pass by quickly. I say Rico: I sorry but need work. Rico no offend, decide sit across room, puff white smoke from pipe, watch work, smoke, look down nose. Very casual thing American upperclass do Saturday morning. Get early bird worm.

SuperBill say: $336,054. Feel like bank make mistake. Check math twice, Wife check too. No mistake. Take check from checkbook, write

$2,038 on check, put in envelope, lick glue that taste medical. Remind that Wife be in hospital soon for birth of pea-in-pod. Only six week away, belly look like full moon. When wife working, have good money for family. Wife fall in love w/ me at jobsite back when she work. She house architect, I house foreman contractor. I stay after hour do more work, no complain about bad measurement or silly architect design. She like hard worker, someone find American dream for her. We go on date to restaurant in Fremont. I drive half-ton dump truck, only car have. She say, I love dump truck. Spend $104 on dinner, dim sum, wife get food on every cart come by. American consumer never say no, no is sign of poor. Wife say she feel pregnant at end of first meal. Hold belly. Oh my, she say, I ate so much I feel pregnant.

Two month later, she pregnant w/ baby, not food. Hold stick w/ two line, two line mean pregnant. Maybe Wife poke hole in condom, marry guy right away. No sure, but wife clever and lazy, make bad combination. Smart girl, have college degree, learn computer program to design house, but no work much, spend time on personal pregnancy leave. When get pregnant, I decide we marry. Tell her I give her American dream by work hard. She sigh, say sound good to her, she no want work much. Have beautiful wedding, small, twenty close family and friend, backyard of house where I remodel kitchen. Have most beautiful understate American wedding at house on water, right on Sound. Wife look like a million buck, American saying, in dimming light of Indian summer day. I love you, say for first time. She look at belly, look at diamond ring, look at me, say, I love you too. I promise honeymoon someday soon, when good time financially, when Wife not on personal pregnancy leave.

After have baby, go American honeymoon, tropical place where lay on beach, drink drink w/ straw and buy silly souvenir. Come home, show neighbor, Look this souvenir make by local people; they look so poor; we support them when buy souvenir. They say, Gracias, gracias, look so thankful. We say, Thank you for trinket that help remember honeymoon forever and ever. But no honeymoon yet. Will come soon, but honeymoon big moneysuck.

Rico job on 31st close to done. Need only do finish work, mount flatscreen television, install appliance. Rico no want dishwasher, but need espresso maker. Espresso maker sign of American upperclass. In Magnolia, only have one neighbor who no have espresso maker, old couple who live in neighborhood for thirty year and give bad fruitcake during holiday progressive dinner. Progressive dinner never come to my home, but will, someday, when place on Prosper finish. Wife design house on Prosper in spare time, when no read. Draw big open kitchen plan w/ stone countertop and dining room table w/ white candle that burn for candlelight dinner at home w/ family of four round table, while dog lay on ground and chew bone.

Sometime at night walk through house on Prosper. Look at room w/ flashlight and see future vision that sit on horizon: big open kitchen w/ stone countertop and dining room table full of neighbor who laugh, drink wine, pat one another on shoulder. Tonight find graffiti in kitchen. Teenager break in through back door, kick in lock and spray-paint countertop, ceiling and refrigerator. Steal microwave oven that no-work anyway. Teenage pull out stove and try light fire in oven, or so it seem. Can burn down house, think. Burn down house no bad option, get insurance claim, money help build house. Notice behind stove there dry rot. No notice before and no big issue, replace wall anyway when expand kitchen. But real-estate lie, she tell me that no dry rot in house, very well-built in 1960s, like old American car, build very well. We have saying in construction: Thank God they no build like use to. Dry rot example, construction saying ring true. Not all saying ring true.

No open Superbill, no yet, leave on table. Right now, need job. Good thing come to those who wait, American proverb. Eastern proverb say, Before you have thirst, dig well. I need go find work, work no come if wait; Eastern proverb better than American proverb. Call old job, see if need new work. One lady say, Yes, I need my bathroom remodeled in Whistler.

Where Whistler? I say.

Oh it's a beautiful place, she say and tell me it look like scene from American painter painting.

I say, No can work in Canada, no permit.

Right, lady say, it's across the border.

No, say, can cross border, just no Canada permit. Need Canada license.

Lady say, It's okay, I never go to Whistler anyway—too many foreigners.

Hang up phone. Call other client. No one need work. When call client on 31st he say, Have you seen Rico? He's run away.

No, say. Why Rico run away when have new mother-in-law New York City studio?

Rico has Alzheimer, he say.

Oh, say. That too bad. If see Rico, I take to mother-in-law.

Thanks, he say, I don't want him getting in trouble.

All day Wife read book to pea-in-pod and Kid. Dog lay on couch, by place where sleep. Wife spend $132 on book for kid last month. Book big moneysuck. What point of library? I say. Free American library, most democrat place in country. Wife shake head, like I no understand. Kid run up to me and throw arms round legs, like hold on for dear life, American saying. Wife say, I think our girl's going to be really intelligent.

How you know? I say.

Because she kicks to the rhythms of poetry.

Hopefully no be poet, I say. Poet no make money.

Right, wife say. By the way, aren't you done with Bertona?

I nod.

And you finished Rico's mother-in-law?

Nod again. Feel caught. See Wife line of thinking and no optimistic about where it go.

So what are you working on?

I think about lie. No hurt Wife, probably. But American saying, Honesty best policy. Still, can make truth seem better than real truth. Can bend truth. Little white lie, American saying, lie that no stain person. Black lie bad lie. White lie, okay.

Tomorrow, I go back to Bertona for client punch list, say.

Oh, let's hope so, she say. Pat stomach. Pick up book, continue read.

Pea-in-pod due two week. Wife complain no sleep. Kid complain, Mom no sleep, Kid no sleep. Think, maybe move in house on Prosper w/ three bedroom. If fix up small thing, broken window, graffiti, maybe move in for little while, then remodel later when wife work. Maybe house on Prosper no so bad, right now. Go to house, see if can live. Turn on flashlight, see big damage. Lot of wall broken. All copper pipe stolen in total clean out. Get angry, throw hammer through drywall. Make perfect hammer shape in drywall, like American cartoon.

Next morning go Bertona. Lawyer client happy to see me. Lawyer nice guy, family sit round table in morning, eat breakfast. Espresso maker grind coffee for Lawyer and Wife, brew in perfect white cup. Place on counter. Lawyer offer me cup of espresso. Best coffee I taste in entire life. Think, I give firstborn child, American saying, to drink coffee that taste like perfect white cup of espresso every morning.

Lawyer say, You know, we've been thinking of remodeling our kitchen in Kihei.

Yes, say. Yes always good answer.

And we want you to do it. It'd be cheaper to have you do it and, we thought, you can spend some time in Hawaii; it could be nice for you and your family.

Yes, say.

We'd like to have it done soon, by the end of May.

That possible, say. Think of honeymoon for wife and family.

Think you can start in two weeks?

Two week wife have baby. But no choice. Need work for money, money for house, house for family, money/house/family for American dream. I say, I start right away!

Ha-ha, lawyer say. Great. We've got renters this week, but how about next Tuesday?

Yes, say.

Perfect.

I go home, want to tell wife we go Hawaii. Right as open door, before word come out mouth, she say, My water broke! Wife no lie. Her pant big wet stain near crotch. She throw book at me, say, I need to go to the hospital right now!

Yes, say. Get in car, drive hospital. Hospital big moneysuck. Hold wife hand, she squeeze hard. Kid sleep in chair outside room like angel. Hospital very nice place. Good place to live. Clean, bright, even have stone counter in reception. Water save feature in bathroom, very modern, stainless steel. Only thing that no is nice is coffee pot in lobby. Coffee pot very middle class.

Wife push out baby girl, pretty baby like gift from Wife. Have lovely family. Wife look tired, like work hard for first time. She pull sweaty hair from face and smile big. Wife happy to push baby from belly. Happy wife, happy life, American saying. American dream to have family with two kid. Very happy to have boy and girl, two healthy kid. Feel like lucky man in world. Drink middle class coffee as celebrate.

Next day, wife come from hospital with baby wrap in blanket and big bill. Wonder what health insurance do, beside big moneysuck. Need tell wife about Hawaii. Say, I go Hawaii next Tuesday. Wife face drop. She hold up wrap baby and look at toddler and shrug shoulder. I say, Good thing go Hawaii, need money, have honeymoon. You come Hawaii in three week, after finish demo. Plus, for two week have lot of room here in house on Bertona. Place in Hawaii kitchen remodel, for lawyer client with happy family and espresso. Wife shake head. Say, Unbelievable, you're going to leave your wife with your newborn baby and your three-year old Son? Wife shake head. I say, We have honeymoon w/o big moneysuck, client pay plane flight, make $5K off kitchen remodel, one month. Wife go to room, slam door. Feel like house shake down to foundation. Wife no happy. Life no happy. Open Superbill on table, write check for $2,038.

Hawaii nice place. Very quiet. Sit on lanai watch sun set over water like big fiery tear drop. Sun make eye glossy right at horizon, same place as American dream. Wife call many time for two week, say thing later regret, use American racial slur. Can hear baby in background cry real loud. Son in background cry, too. Whole symphony of family come through phone, while sit on lanai and watch sun set over water like tear of fire. Very quiet once hang up. Also, sleep in bed on Hawaii, first time three year. Bed very comfortable design for sleep. Work go quick: finish demo, measure cabinet, order flooring and stone counter, appliance deliver. Appliance sit in living room like quiet stainless steel family.

Wife come after two week. Say, I swear to God if you ever do that again I will kill you. Very serious look on face. Put baby in hand, Kid wrap arms around legs, hold on for dear life. Wife go to lanai, sit down, ask for drink. She want drink with straw and little umbrella like mini party. I say, Don't have drink, alcohol big moneysuck. Wife say, Get me the drink now! Very serious look on face, so I walk to hotel down beach, get drink, bring to wife. Can bring glass to hotel tomorrow, or keep as souvenir from honeymoon.

Wife say house on Prosper have notice on front door. Look like official notice. Wife no read notice, say it be there when get back. Why worry on honeymoon? Wife smile around straw. No seem worry. It work out, Wife say. Kid go to bed in own bedroom for first time in life. Baby fall asleep in arms. Sit on lanai w/ wife at night. Very quiet and warm; white light come from big moon in dark sky w/ lot of star. No bug in Hawaii; can hear wave crash on shore. Hawaii like little slice of heaven, American saying.

Superbill waiting at home when back from Hawaii. Say: $332,866. Write check for $2,038. Notice hand tan from Hawaii, hand no look like American skin color.

Hawaii great honeymoon. Wife and family very happy. Work hard during day, sit on lanai w/ Wife during night. Have good talk, watch dark sky and quiet ocean. Feel lucky to live part of American dream. First night back in Seattle feel full of optimism, walk dog round neighborhood, look in warm window and feel like dream happen very soon for family. Feel that boot strap help pull up. See family w/ two kid eat meal at table while laugh hard and parent drink wine. Walk dog by window very slow. Decide, since in happy mood, will walk past house on Prosper, see house for family.

House on Prosper have notice on front door. Read: IMPORTANT NOTICE OF INTENT TO ACQUIRE OWNERSHIP OF AN ABANDONED HOME. Delinquent owner, notice say, abandon four month, want take over 45 day from notice. No think this legal; I legal own house. Notice is sign by real-estate, who sell house. Feel like scam. Go home, show wife. Wife say no look like scam, cite Occ. Code: §1201.217 in second paragraph, look legitimate. Next morning,

can call. No need worry. American law protect American homeowner.

Next morning call and say no is scam. Lady on phone very polite. American way of show pity. Need prove home no abandon. Need prove through bill to address. But no have. Have all mail go to Bertona rental. Only bill have from four month ago, when buy house. No bill for four month, real-estate know. I call real-estate, she no answer. Then get phone call, but no is real-estate, is client on 31st, ask if see Rico.

No see Rico, be in Hawaii for one month.

Nice, client say, my family does that every year, too. Very fun. So you haven't seen Rico?

No see Rico, but keep eye out.

Rico has a disease called Alzheimers, he say.

Yes, I say, you tell before.

It's not too severe, he say. The weed helps control it, but sometimes Rico runs away.

We find, say. No too many green Impala in Magnolia.

Well, he say, I worry about Rico. Rico does a lot of crazy things.

Hang up and call company turn on gas and electricity, send bill right away. Bill take two month. Call company turn on water, say same, two month. No can get bill for sixty day. Wife look over top of book, say, What are you going to do now? Now go find real-estate, say.

Drive real-estate office, but no one there. It Wednesday. American real-estate no work Wednesday? Call real-estate again, get voicemail. When get home, wife look up from book, say, I think we need a nanny, I'm tired of taking care of two kids. Nanny very American upperclass, so wife may be right. Plus, wife think about return work real soon. When wife work, have money for nanny, plus nanny make more time for work on Prosper house.

You need to relax, wife say. It'll all work out. Let's talk about this nanny.

Sit on couch, talk to wife, look out window at street, feel like lanai in Hawaii, but w/o sunset because cloud like big wool blanket over sun. Talk and think how nice have nanny and four bedroom house on Prosper. Sky move from gray to black.

Tonight cold night. No moon, no star, only cloud. City light reflect in cloud like warm orange glow. Walk dog round neighborhood, go toward Prosper house, think be nice to see American dream at night. See water tower in distance, more lit up than remember, have warm orange glow, like cloud. Maybe city install light to keep teenager from graffiti. But when round corner, see light is fire from Prosper. House on fire. Flame roll out window and burn up garage. Fire make eye water, blurry watery vision see house, like sunset in Hawaii. Look round, see if neighbor see fire. See green sparkle turn corner.

Run dog back to rental house on Bertona. Call 911, tell house is on fire. Then grab wife, baby, son, dog, and run back to water tower. House on Prosper still on fire. American fire truck take long time. Stand across street under water tower and watch house burn. Think, if only water tower burst, water put out fire, drop water on house, save house, keep house preserve. But water tower no move. Water tower very high, protect by chain fence w/ barb wire and teenage graffiti. House keep burn. American fire truck still no come. On cold night, house fire feel warm, even from cross street, it feel like beautiful huge fireplace that burn in special time to keep family warm in tender moment. Have wonderful family that hold tight. Wife read book in light of fire, baby no cry, Son no say anything. Fire make cold air ripple like wavy sunset. House like big orange tear drop.

LEAVE HER A HUT AS WELL

EZRY REVELLE

Sea waves are green and wet, / But up from where they die, / Rise others vaster yet, / And those are brown and dry.

—**"Sand Dunes" by Robert Frost**

LIVING ROOM

Beach stretched thinner than the strained telephone wires, strung late century and obsolete. Yards fenced, filled with sand and plaster anchors, covered with sand, speckled and sun baked. Driveways for one car and manatee mailboxes and green palms with brown fronds like skirts and collars stud the one thoroughfare. Houses pose empty.

HALLWAY

While autumnal winds carried the storms from another hemisphere over the sea, the coastline further down this strand crumbled. Across the tides it dissipated then congressed onto the ocean floor. Until it pooled the cove, lobbed from wave armament. Through the front door and gathered into piles.

BALCONY

House, grey-shingled, yellow-stuccoed. Windows Bahama shuttered, dropped grey moss gathered, propped open and awning. Interiors snagged the shell-strewn highwater mark with their scrolling border designs, their embellished aluminum sconces, and their flower boxes, top layer full of ocean bed cobblestone. Patio door shattered, dunes awaited Dido.

BEDROOM

Dido could count to ten-thousand in as many seconds, but had no capacity in which to weigh the granules occupying what should be her patio. She possessed that kindliness useful in depositions and a memory that contained a figment of ceramic tile. Her wearied-straight hair caught in silver link necklace as her purse was excavated. Buyer called Realtor.

DINING ROOM

Said Buyer, "The first floor's missing." Said Realtor, "We haven't cleaned it yet; we were going to start renting in December." Said Buyer, "Where am I supposed to live—

upstairs and enjoy the view or downstairs and dig myself a sandcastle?" Said Realtor, "Somewhere else."

BATHROOM

Meant Buyer: "Why didn't you tell me this why didn't I anticipate this why haven't I fixed this what is this what kind of place is this what do I do with / in a kind of place like this?" Meant Realtor: "Of course not why should we what type of person purchases in October off-season immediately no questions I should not be expected to." Meant Buyer: "Lady, I'll show you expectation and so much lemonade from these lemons." Meant Realtor: "Somewhere else, Bitch."

KITCHEN

Hangs up cell phone about to be recalled. Pulls off palm frond dilapidated and hovering on leafstalk cordage. Smacks sand to disturb slumbering mites and to remember the contractor's number. Digs stem-sized trenches.

ATTIC

Hours counted by sun as dial four to twelve until contractors available are restlessness. Envious of those grey moss spindles, rootless, so easy to dislodge and please. Drift of sand of so much disappointment. Beach thin and strung and straining.

JESSICA BEBENEK

ART IS FOR FUCK-UPS

"Someone used to hit me there,"
you say into my neck and I can't
see your eyes, but your throat
makes a sound like coarse facial hair
as you laugh through a smile which
isn't really a smile at all.
You hit my hand away when I touched
your bare chest, the fabric over your soft dick,
and flipped Stevens's *Tillerman*
for something to listen to.

"What's a nice way to say dick,"
you mused from your nesting hollow
where wit drips through your fingertips
like a fine sieve and time stops
for hours. Your passion excited me
and so I said "hardness" and thought
darling, you're marvellous, just marvellous
in your beauty and your sexlessness.

"Who would have thought this is all I really wanted,"
you said—but I thought it when the music played,
when your hands curved into me, hands
that carve meaning, hands that know

the key to shaping words delicate as milk glass.
But it's your stillness, your silence,
your refinement of our complete beings
into precise lines.
You make us barely an existence
and more alive than life.

"Things will get better for you," I say
even though, in our fantasy,
you're Donnie and I'm Cherita.
Because I hope that my words will be silent,
that you will inhale my breath.
I hope that the music will stop
and that time will keep going.
Because I hope that our bodies will come
close enough to fall apart entirely.

JESSICA BEBENEK WIRES

There is a street and you are
the young woman crouching in short
heels and a flat flapper chest in
a pale, pleated dress, curbside. And
the curb is a rolling, crashing
wave on pointed toes, spraying
splinters of red brick and the air
in its darkness and its coldness
doesn't seem quite fair to that girl
who is you, whose hand
is pressed to a pole.

There is a geometry in this
air and in this architecture
there is a pattern—or a rhythm
in the intersection of parallel lines
mystically twisting. The swan-necked
isosceles triangle of the lamppost
crux is a gateway to images
of telephone wires stretching like
tendons in the neck of a dark-
skinned dancer in gold Lycra.

The noirish groan of a solitary
streetlamp spotlight, freezing
your bones into shards of stark
white ice—cut and paste
pool of yellow light
on purple cement sidewalk
spotted in black gum
so weather-beaten that it too
has turned to stone.

HOW TO ENTER A ROOM

MICHAEL PECK

This is how you don't enter a room.

With an overambitious smile twitching at your mouth like the middle part of a flowering lunacy.

Or with the synthetic stench of your exploded hairspray container, not just rolling off your sable curls, but providing a visible patina around you.

You especially don't enter a room wearing a cocktail-stained white cocktail dress, the dry martini splash blazing fadedly on the waist.

All of this is exactly how you don't enter a room.

And all of this is exactly how you've entered this one.

Eyes switch to you for seconds. Two hundred eyes calculating how wrongly you've entered this room. You stand there almost wittily slapstick in your silence until everyone has ADHD'd your erroneous entrance and resumed not noticing.

Plush armchairs and sofas, gauche decor comprised of hanging textiles, sepulchral avant-garde lighting, a flare for tasteless objets d'art that typify nothing.

And:

The room billows with fluttery crepe and central-air. Caterers bash into one another with trays, bustling through the dressed-up banqueters like mad rivers diverging, bowing in an out of conversations.

You've entered this room and now you don't know how to enter this room.

While the people gesturing is a nightmare you've had recently.

A shaven-headed man, crumpling a napkin in his hand, points at the ceiling and scoffs. Then the woman beside you—a peripheral flash of yellow silk scarf, bangs, horrifying cordiality—breathes into your ear, "The tortes are unbelievable," and then you say something, watching a man in a bright red vest saunter through the cliques with a bottle of wine in each hand. Watching a girl play the piano so softly in a corner that the music goes unheard. Watching four women in the same dress remarking on the coincidence and laughing.

Watching yourself watching yourself watching.

You move stealthily to the buffet table. You nibble on the chocolate tortes. Five or six, at least.

The woman in the yellow scarf: "Aren't they?"
You: Mumble.

Can you un-enter a room? Not just leave a room. But erase you're having been there in the first place?

Now as you dip into the chocolate, pleased and on the verge of moving, yes, on the verge of moving your entire self. Right on the margin of this decision: a fresh problem.

Everyone starts to pour out of the room and into the lobby, and soon the room is vacated except for the fragile girl at the piano.

And you right there in the midst of scurrying staff Windexing the windows, tearing down the decor, scraping table-clothes with razorblades. You right there in the midst of this because you also don't know how to correctly exit a room.

ANDREW RUZKOWSKI

CONDITIONALS

If thinking

    like a river

  then gutter.

       If water

       then dirt.

If like a wind

    then   [ ]   beneath

    feather,   then up.

    If blood   then eat

  organ meat.

      Vessels and vesicles and bicycles.

If a wheel

then chain,

then oil and soot.

If ash,   an aspen

then white   then paper.

If fibrous then weave

a set of twigs.

If sweep then concrete   then gray.

If pebble then a glass

of water,

then a crow.

If black then space,

then angle,

then being.

ANDREW RUZKOWSKI

CAUTION CAUTION CAUTION
CAUTION CAUTION
CAUTION

l   l
        e   e
e   a   a   a
a   f   v   v
v   e   e
e   s   s
s

Cardinalis   to mouth   to mark   [Insert Haiku
Here]
    cardinalis   your scars   my song.

                 Something   tethered.
A guest leaving.   I heard   the words
                Stasis in   *darkness.*

     Red on sun
on red.

Look into

     a form.

Perhaps morn

       ing.

                                        A low-

ceilinged sky.

                                        Ground

aching frost.
If I could say

       something,   The tree

looks
corrugated.
feed you.

          Mouth   I think it's

dying.

                                        M. eats

leaves.

                                      My flesh

feels

                                      stranger

than.

just

doubt it.

just

tired.

Maybe I'm

cold but I

Maybe I'm

dying or

I want my street to be a waterway and my park to be green but concrete is ok too, I
suppose. M. would rather have it be green and I think she's right about this one.

I think M. is a master of bushido.
For her beautiful muscles tell me so.

When I sleep I imagine her skinless. She is not dead and tells me to make the
fucking park green.

Two options: alchemy or write the alderman.

CAUTION   CAUTION   CAUTION
CAUTION

                    l   l

                    e   e
        e
                    a   a   a
        a
                    f   v   v

        v

e   e   e

                                                                     s   s

      e

s

Cold air sticks
to the body.

This shouldn't amaze
me but it does.
                                                                                                      Something like a

membrane.
I can hear gunshots
in my sternum.

                                                                                                      Do you hear them?

I like the sound of
the word percuss.

                                                                                                      So radiantly being.

My sound is
percussive and

                                                                                                      my ears freeze

white.
Gunshots make
percussive sounds,

                                                                                                      directly under my

bedroom,

always in

alleyways.

I see

                        a silence   intricate

                                                now forming

                                                            my song.

It feels

                    painted   or ancient

                                            I can't tell

                                                        or hear.

I keep

                    a set   of strings

                                            to pluck

my throat.

A silence
        might be   a thing

                    felt

                            or missed.

Might be
        absence   of sound

            or all sound

                        present.

        All sound,

                    a film.

ANDREW RUZKOWSKI

POST-THOUGHT THOUGHTS:

I like living in sound.

I think M. is really a sound.

I look at pictures of distant nebulae to make me slightly less scared of what people call
impending doom.

The pictures are noise in portraiture.

The noise is a being.

M. tells me:

*I see ten thousand miles of nowhere. I gaze into forests beyond
light. I can see that you   have no mind at all, no mind and surely no talent.*

I enjoy the

fall and want

to make it

a succinct thing.

Perhaps a

single

                        color, probably not orange
        but neon tree bark

                  would be pleasing. I would

like

                  to wear a layer of snow.

ANDREW RUZKOWSKI AUBADE

There were letters walking among our eyelids,
the first drop of day glowing becomes

a glowing kettle. Hear an H snap
a throat like the seagull saying I want,

I want, I want. Say connect a globe to a globe,
say how old and what for and do you remember.

Dwell between things and names, always I.
Always between form and forgotten.

You say forget logic and its symmetry, you say
for the sake of argument tell me you travel

by sonar and I float on soldered beads,
something archipelagic. Tell the day to green

and dip like swallows; tell light to ray your eyes.
Tell sound to leave the deeps of your body

sounding in my room, a breath unhinging
in unhinging sky. Think atmospheric.

Even the squared stillness with slack-jawed
sleep, with shudders. Think a dream equation.

The hour speaks through windows: come in,
come in and taste slick fat and flame.

No matter the intervals between light,
sound begins and begins and begins.

Think floating. Think something lopsided
turning, something bent and bending.

Taste glossolalia and speak salt and mutter
and matter. Tear through a sheet and dwell.

Think whistling. Such a small want disclosed.
For the sake of being lift your throat, an island.

THE SHAKERS

JENNIFER SKY

We are the Shakers, Children of God. His Love shines in our daily ways as it does in our worship. We do not believe in the ways of flesh, for denying the body is to give ourselves to God.

Christ is whom we seek in the dark.

His hair-covered arms circle our waists and draw us down toward the thump of hard heaven.

Our growth, true and thick is in our land. Our wheat stalks reach toward His light. Felling our trees is a kind ritual. The grazing of sharp iron against wood. Splinters taking flight, as would a flock of morning birds. Wood to be thinned, trimmed, heated, and cooked. Shaped and nailed to create straight-back seats, a thing where an angel would come to rest. You can hear our rhythmic pounding far away, into the fields, into our churches' sanctum.

We work our bodies hard, and so what would be left for a man, a woman, to enjoy after dark?

Shakers are not made by birth. We are a calling you come to. A calling you choose for yourself. A calling you understand. No children will come of this contract.

No breath in your ear or pressure between your legs.

Our celibacy is a most sacred belief. A way to bring ourselves closer to Christ. We did know this could lead to the death of our belief. For the way to grow a religion is to bear children into it. The fattening of the flock outside, from within.

Yet, Mother Ann's teachings were of the separation of man and woman. Separation from those whose arms move in that way as the ax swings. Separation from those whose bodies create that bittersweet smell after a day in the fields; that which make some of us want to wear their work clothes just to keep smelling it.

Separation from he who caught our eye when we bent to transfer the dishes or whose finger grazed our palm in the middle of a Sabbath worship dance.

Our looms are held tight.

Our fabrics are the best of quality; this water-resistant silk almost as well known as our dancing. In Sabbath's Sanctuary Hall, men and women separate into rows, our hands flung high.

Our bodies in circles. Shaking. Watching the other. Heads and hands dipping in perfect unison.

Our God is both female and male, equal and layered. Our dancing, ring-around bodies, the girls on the inside, boys on the outside. Wrapping over top. Writhing and shouting. Hands shaking. Singing out. Praising His/Her name.

We are the Shakers, Children of God. His Love shines in our daily ways as it does in our worship. We do not believe in the ways of flesh, for denying the body is to give ourselves to God. Christ is whom we seek in the dark. His hair-covered arms circle our waists and draw us down toward the thump of hard heaven.

ORAL HYGIENE

KATHERINE KARLIN

The dentist who supervised my incoming adult teeth was Dr. Ira Mindel, a sad, square-faced man who shared a practice with his identical twin, and whose noirish transom cast on his waiting room a sea-foam light, as if all of us patients were suspended in the hull of an intimate ship laded with back copies of Highlights for Children. We traveled the fifteen miles to Mineola even though there were many good dentists closer at hand, because, my mother said, the Drs. Mindel were "friends of Uncle Norman."

For a man of dyspeptic temperament, my Uncle Norman had a lot of friends: the dentists, the clothier who outfitted us for camp, the grocer who fished the fattest pickle from the barrel to give me free of charge. I never saw any of these men together, not at a picnic or at a deli, and although they shared the same defeated posture I wondered how good friends they could possibly be, who never visited. Not until I was an adult did I understand they had all been members of the Communist Party, all washed up on the shore.

Dr. Ira gave me fillings. He administered nitrous oxide, which distorted the Eydie Gorme soundtrack in his office, and, somewhat perversely, he gave me a lollipop for my troubles. I liked the nitrous oxide more than I liked the lollipop. "This will hurt a little," he said, and I respected his candor. "But not for very long."

At a point in my sister's life and mine, Dr. Ira recommended we see Dr. Bernard Grubar, the orthodontist, as we would soon be aware of how we looked to boys. We each got a bite plate, and I joined a vast and smug sorority, sucking the pink crustaceous plate from my hard palate, its hills and valleys bearing the impress of my own gums, and setting it on my cafeteria tray while I lunched, in happy sync with the other girls. From time to time, when I climb out of a pool or eat macaroni and cheese, I still thump the roof of my mouth to see if it's in place. My sister, who was already going to parties and rock concerts, kissing boys and smoking grass, and who, when she was home, retreated to her bedroom and scored her sullenness with T. Rex, kept her bite plate in its original carrying case, buried in a drawer of bulky sweaters. At our follow-up, Dr. Grubar probed my molars with his stubby fingers and shook his jowls at me. "I can't help you if you're not wearing your bite plate," he said. "Why can't you be more like your sister?"

With the taste of his thumbprints in my mouth and a fresh sense of injustice, I stood between my parents and the Dick Cavett show to voice my indignation. My mother, in a plume of cigarette smoke, said, "Don't go back."

"Really?" I asked, ready with an arsenal of justifications.

"The man's an idiot," my father said.

"Just don't go back."

And with that I quit orthodonture.

I grew up, I moved away, I worked jobs without insurance, I neglected my teeth. One morning I woke up with a man and my pillow was stiff with blood. I pulled the Houston Yellow Pages, fat as a baby, onto my lap and searched for a Jewish name in the dental listings, finally settling on a Dr. Mordecai Schatz. He wore a jeweler's loupe on his glasses that magnified his eye. "How long has it been since you've had a check up?"

"A ong ime," I said.

"You have periodontal disease," he said as he washed his hands. "But not to worry. Everything can be fixed." I made an appointment for a deep plane and clean, and saw him every three months thereafter, blooming under his care. He advised me to get myself to a periodontist who could remove my wisdom teeth. "I got a terrific guy," he said, and he gave me a phone number, but the periodontist did not have a Jewish name so I never called. What did I need anyone else for? I had Dr. Schatz! He moved about his tiny cubicle with such grandfatherly agility and focus. He told me about his pro bono work, fixing teeth in Peru, in Bangladesh. He told me that among the old people he treated, their contentedness with life was directly related to the number of original teeth in their heads. "Eating with teeth, Miss Simon, is a pleasure!"

Staring at a stain on his dropped ceiling, I wondered if Dr.

Schatz could detect my bad behavior through my gums, like a phrenologist; I wondered if he knew I went to Galveston with two boys I didn't know very well, and went down on one, and then the other. Not because I was pressed. Because I had some idea that expressing an uninhibited appetite for sex would make me feel capricious and free-spirited. It only made me feel old. But all he said, as he massaged my labial gingiva, was, "Miss Simon, please get those wisdom teeth removed. It's a question of hygiene."

I met a mechanic who loved music so much he fixed Lyle Lovett's car for free. He didn't care about Galveston: when we walked into a club, we parted the seas. He promised to make me soup if I got my wisdom teeth removed, so I made an appointment with the goyishe periodontist and got it done, all four on a Friday afternoon, and spent the weekend in bed with the mechanic watching "Marathon Man" and taking Advil, eager to return to Dr. Schatz and show him my progress.

It turned out I married a man over wisdom teeth. Not the mechanic. Another man I met, a few years later, a gentile but a righteous one, whose overbite is so pronounced I can wriggle my pinky between his uppers and lowers while his jaw is clenched. He too was told to remove his wisdom teeth. He wasn't insured but I was so we married. He never did get his wisdom teeth removed, but we are still married. He sleeps with a mouthguard to prevent grinding, so every morning it's like I wake up with an NFL star.

We moved to Los Angeles, where I put myself under the care of Dr. Sakamoto. He was not a Jew but I gave him special dispensation because he was born in a concentration camp: Manzanar. Dr. Sakamoto had the long fingers of a violinist—his touch was light and his office spacious, and when he sat on his stool his fingers spread like elegant spider legs on his thighs. It was Dr. Sakamoto who first alerted me to the healing properties of kale. He had two daughters at Berkeley—one a filmmaker, the other a pianist—and he worried about their futures but was glad, after all, that they were creative. "It's always good to be creative," he said, hooking a saliva extractor on my lower lip. "It's what separates us from the savage beasts."

Around this time the industry shifted; more and more my care was administered by the hygienists, tireless women with spit-speckled eyeglasses and crepe-soled shoes. My favorite was Lorelei, a Filipina in her early thirties, who garaged hardware in my mouth as she regaled me with stories about her and her homegirls: ribald bachelorette parties, drunken baby showers, high-rolling weekends in Vegas. Lorelei knew how to have a good time. Wherever she traveled she went to Sam's Club to price Waterpiks and electric toothbrushes so she could pass the savings on to her patients. Lorelei had a cousin who was the karaoke champion of Manila. He was so famous a Philippines-based beer company sponsored his karaoke tour of the Pacific Rim.

"Unh?" I said.

"Karaoke is big in the Philippines," she explained. When he came to L.A., though, he disrespected the family, denying them comps and refusing to take his and Lorelei's mutual grandmother for a ride in his complimentary limo, which Lorelei's lola would have loved. As she measured my distals, her disappointment was fresh. "Nobody ever gets too big to be from where they're from," she said reasonably.

Now we live in a place where there is no Jewish dentist for a hundred miles. Instead, I have a dentist who urges me to accept Jesus as my lord and savior. But I see him only once a year, and briefly; my maintenance is entrusted to a black woman named Diane. Her firm cheeks are like rubber balls, so close to mine as she works I could kiss them. She encourages my habits, and she praises my flossing technique even when I don't deserve praise. She hands me a mirror that I don't want; my face is a hard landscape. "You see this here?" She scratches her curette against the bare cervix of a lower canine. "That right there will be exposed until the day you go to your glory. Nothing you can do but to keep it from getting worse."

That goyishe periodontist back in Houston removed my wisdom teeth in December, during a week of Texas floods. When the rain stopped, a turtle the size of steering wheel walked up the driveway to my door, as if he were delivering mail, his head craning from side to side. I got a letter canceling my appointment with Dr. Schatz because sadly, he had died during the storm. I stared at that comma, ferreting out its meaning. Was it sad for the letter-writer to inform us of his death, or did Dr. Schatz in fact die sadly, his shiny Hollenbacks and burnishers beyond his reach? Either way, I would never get to show him that at last I had heeded his instruction.

Shortly after that the mechanic died in a drunk driving accident. He was the drunk. He'd spent the day floating down the Brazos with his friends, one inner tube tied to another and the last stocked with cold beer, the river hard on the water and on their teeth. That same moment, my mother in New York was navigating the capacity of her new Brothers word processor when her gums bled spontaneously, like a saint's, and the capillaries burst in her eyeballs. Eight months later she was dead. And then my father dropped a bicuspid in the scrub of the seventh fairway and he never smiled again; six weeks later he was dead. My sister married a hedge fund manager and drinks hot coffee through a straw to prevent dental stains; we rarely speak. I still ritually touch the tip of my tongue to the dimpled beds of my missing teeth, one for each of the ghosts who are with me: my father, my mother, my lover, my beloved dentist.

By my reckoning I have spent ten whole days in the dentist's chair: a European vacation, or a brief and intense affair. I still have my silver fillings, older than most of my friends, and even though my current doctor offers to replace them with epoxy, to do so would be to dishonor the memory of Dr. Ira, my uncle's comrade, now long dead. My body is in decline; my knuckles click like cicadas. But I have my 28 teeth, and I can name every man and woman who labored to maintain them, whose faces hovered over mine like the moon, who offered me enduring advice: This will hurt, but only a little; be more like your sister; be creative, eat kale; eating with teeth is a pleasure; you will never outgrow where you're from; the mistakes that you make will be yours until the day you go to your glory.

To whom should I pray?

To the suffering part of an opened-up oyster. To swarms of bees. To polymer glue. To planeloads of the falsely accused.

To answer your question: To dumb luck.

How can "I" let go of "myself?"

Recall that we have yet to encounter a single species of archipelago into which we have not insinuated ourselves with savage fires and ink.

Recall further that you were sad once, that you held it up as an example of the nondescript machinery of that moment you know is coming, where your dreams unroll to meet you behind your re-animated house.

To answer your question: It takes reality and just a little Kevlar. Pray for the city to be cleared of people.

Why isn't the power of sight absolute?

One day you flip a rock over. Life or something to the effect of life teems below. It is cool there, under the trees, just over the earth. You sleep. You dream that you walk on the faces of your enemies. It is a good day, though winter is on its way on hands and knees to the foot of your bed.

Such days are rare. You couldn't express yourself in such enormous mouthfuls without them.

This is one way of saying that there are still a few ways of becoming heavier than the evils that are brewing against us.

But, to answer your question: You wouldn't want to watch us teasing out our differences.

HATCHET
LANA STOREY

1

o bury the hatchet, you have to catch it first. This is the difficult part. The person still throwing will not be likely to make this part easy for you.

If the weapon parts your hair, it has come close. If the weapon splits hairs, closer. If the weapon parts the sea, it is indeed a divine weapon. Or throw. Or thrower. Or there is something really mystical going on. If you see mist gathering to obscure your vision, look harder. Don't take your eye off the axe.

If the hatchet is the thing that parts the two of you, I'm surprised. I would have guessed something had already come between you. At this advanced stage, there's no looking back. There's only trying not to take your eye off the flying object.

When things get sharp, there's only the ground for comfort. The dull, hard earth to lie down on. But it's only comfortable to lie down when you know the blade is below you, buried, not coming for you anymore. Plus, this way, you can't be tempted to make the next throw.

Unless you dig it up, after all that. But it would be a lot of trouble. It would have to be worth it.

But before you can do anything, you have to catch that hatchet, and I can't tell you how it's done. I've never done it before, or seen it done, except maybe once, in a dream, when I woke up on the ground and dug dirt out from under my fingernails and felt for the part in my hair and felt for you.

2 (AN ADDENDUM)

Sometimes the other person will have already done all the hard work, and all you've done is dug it up, thinking it a root vegetable, or hidden treasure. Or a sharp axe.

Because after all, you're always right.

But then you'd better mean it.

CONTRIBUTORS' NOTES

BECKY ADNOT-HAYNES is a doctoral student at the University of Cincinnati, where she is the associate editor of *Cincinnati Review*. She has published short fiction in *Missouri Review*, *Indiana Review*, *West Branch*, *CutBank*, and elsewhere. Her story "Baby Baby" won the Buffalo Prize and appears in *Hobart*.

MATTHEW ANKENY was born in Long Beach, raised in Orange County, studied in Chicago, fell in love with Seattle, but lives in San Francisco. He is an MFA in Fiction candidate at San Francisco State University. He is currently at work on a collection of short stories. Find out more at matthewankeny.com.

JESSICA BEBENEK is a Toronto poet and writer with work appearing in *Steel Bananas*, *The Flying Walrus*, and *Uncharted Sounds* magazines. She has won several awards through the York University Creative Writing program, is the founder of Loose Ends Press and published her first chapbook, *I, Family*, this past spring.

FRANK BILL has been published in *Granta*, *Playboy*, *Oxford American*, *The New York Times*, *The Daily Beast*, *PANK*, *FSG Work in Progress*, *New Haven Review*, *Talking River Review*, *Plots With Guns*, *Thuglit*, *Beat to a Pulp*, and many other outlets. His first book, *Crimes in Southern Indiana*, was released by Farrar, Straus & Giroux in September 2011 and his first novel, *Donnybrook*, hit bookstores in March 2013. He is agented by Stacia Decker of Donald Maass Literary Agency.

ALICE BRADLEY is a blogger (www.finslippy.com) and co-author of the book *Let's Panic About Babies*. She has written for numerous publications, including *Best Creative Nonfiction*, *The Sun*, *The Onion*, and *Fence*. She was nominated for a Pushcart Prize in nonfiction and received her MFA. from the New School.

CAROLINE CREW edits *ILK*. Her poems have appeared in *Salt Hill*, *H_NGM_N* and *Sixth Finch* among other places. She has a chapbook from Dancing Girl Press. Often she doesn't have a real home but currently she is an MFA candidate at UMass Amherst.

JOSEPH DANTE is a writer from South Florida. His work has been featured in *Monkeybicycle*, *Pear Noir!*, *Paste*, and elsewhere. He is also a reader and lilliputian lackey for *Hobart*. You can find him talking to himself at http://josephdante.com.

GEFFREY DAVIS's debut collection, *Revising the Storm* (BOA Editions 2014), won the 2013 A. Poulin Poetry Prize. He considers the Puget Sound area "home"—though he's been raised by much more of the Pacific Northwest, and now by Central Pennsylvania as well.

CATHY DAY is the author of *The Circus in Winter* (Harcourt 2004) and *Comeback Season* (Free Press 2008). Recently her work has appeared in *The Millions*, *North American Review*, and *Ninth Letter*. She teaches at Ball State University and is on the planning committee for the Midwest Writers Workshop.

RACHEL FRANK is originally from Traverse City, Michigan. She received her AAS from Lansing Community College in 2006. Since graduating, she has traveled to coffee farms in Mexico, and has had her photography published in several magazines and displayed in galleries in Lansing, Traverse City, and Grand Rapids. Currently she is attending Western Michigan University and most recently studied Spanish and culture in Costa Rica and Peru. She can be found online at www.rachelfrankphoto.com.

SAM GRIEVE was born in Cape Town and lived in Paris and London prior to settling down in Connecticut with her family. She has worked as a writer, bookseller and antiquarian book dealer, and her work has recently appeared in *A cappella Zoo*, *Grey Sparrow Journal*, *Wild Violet*, and *Sanskrit*.

AMASA GUY has published four books of creative non-fiction plus research monographs, chapters, and articles. He served for twenty years as editor of research journals. His creative work has been published in *Slipstream* and has been accepted by *JJournal*. Guy lives with his adored wife of 53 years on fifty acres in north Georgia where they raise goats, cattle, a herd of feral cats and a huge loveable dangerous boar named Boaz.

REBECCA HAZELWOOD is an amateur cat-wrangler and MFA graduate living in Kentucky. You can find her obsessing over great poems every week at *Structure and Style* (structureandstyle.tumblr.com).

KATHERINE KARLIN's fiction has appeared in the Pushcart Prize anthology, *New Stories from the South*, and many literary journals. Her short story collection, *SEND ME WORK*, was published by Northwestern University Press in 2011. She teaches at Kansas State University.

AVRAM KLINE lives in Brooklyn and teaches at a public high school. His poems and fiction can be found in *Fence*, *Transom*, *The Common*, *Juked*, *Softblow*, *Prick of the Spindle*, *Action Yes*, and *Jellyfish*. Permafrost will release his chapbook entitled *City* in the fall of 2013.

JENNA LE's first book, *Six Rivers* (New York Quarterly Books 2011), was a Small Press Distribution Poetry Bestseller. Her poems and translations have appeared in *AGNI Online*, *Barrow Street*, *Bellevue Literary Review*, *Massachusetts Review*, *Post Road*, *32 Poems*, and other journals.

LESLIE ANNE MCILROY won the Slipstream Poetry Chapbook Prize, the Word Press Poetry Book Prize for *Rare Space*, and the Chicago Literary Awards. Her second book, *Liquid Like This*, was published by Word Press. Leslie's poems appear in journals like *The Mississippi Review*, the *New Ohio Review* and *Jubilat*. For more, visit lamcilroy.com.

PAULA MENDOZA's poems have appeared or are forthcoming in *The Awl*, *elimae*, and *The Offending Adam*. She has an MFA from the University of Michigan and lives in Austin, TX.

MICHAEL MLEKODAY is the author of *The Dead Eat Everything* (Kent State University Press, 2013). Mlekoday is a National Poetry Slam Champion, and recent work has appeared or is forthcoming in *Ploughshares*, *Ninth Letter*, *Cincinnati Review*, and other journals.

DELANEY NOLAN's fiction and nonfiction has appeared or is forthcoming in *The Chattahoochee Review*, *The South Carolina Review*, *Oxford American,* and elsewhere. She was recently the artist-in-residence at Skriðuklaustur in Iceland. "NO LESBIANS, CHILDREN OR PETS" is a selection from her chapbook *Louisiana Maps*, winner of the 2012 Ropewalk Press Fiction Editor's Chapbook Prize.

MICHAEL PECK's work has appeared in *The Believer*, *Juked*, *Los Angeles Review of Books*, *Identity Theory,* and others. He is a sometime book critic for the *Missoula Independent*, and now lives in Portland, OR. *The Last Orchard in America*, his first novel, was serialized in *The 2nd Hand*.

ALEXIS POPE is the author of the chapbook *Girl Erases Girl* (Dancing Girl Press 2013) and a curator of The Big Big Mess Reading Series. Her work has appeared or is forthcoming in *Washington Square*, *Columbia Poetry Review*, *Guernica*, *Jellyfish*, and *Sixth Finch*, among others. She will soon be another MFA candidate living in Brooklyn.

EZRY REVELLE lives in Boulder, CO, but has previously inhabited such places as Pittsburgh, PA, and Mobile, AL. She's working toward an MFA in Creative Writing from the University of Colorado at Boulder and spends her off-hours translating Pliny & Euripides. This is her first story publication.

LUKE ROLFES grew up in Polk City, IA, and teaches at Northwest Missouri State University. He is a fiction editor at *The Laurel Review*, and his works appears in *Passages North, Bat City Review, Connecticut Review*, and many others journals.

ANDREW RUZKOWSKI lives and writes in Chicago. His poems have appeared in *Columbia Poetry Review, Black Tongue Review, The Camel Saloon, Emerge Literary Journal, Parable Press, The Bakery,* and *Midwestern Gothic*, among others. His chapbook, *A Shape & Sound*, is available from ELJ Publications. He loves Sriracha sauce.

GREGORY SOLANO received his MFA in Creative Writing from the University of Virginia. He lives in a house full of friends in Charlottesville, Virginia.

LANA STOREY is a Canadian writer living in San Diego. Her work appears or is forthcoming in *Joyland, Found Press Quarterly*, and *paperplates*. She received an honorable mention in *San Diego CityBeat's* Fiction 101 contest in 2012. She has an MFA from the University of Guelph.

MICHAEL JOSEPH WALSH currently lives in Fairfax, VA, and is the poetry editor for *Phoebe: A Journal of Literature and Art*. His work has appeared or is forthcoming in *Fence, DIAGRAM*, and *RealPoetik*. In the fall he will be a PhD candidate in Creative Writing at the University of Denver.

DANIEL ENJAY WONG is currently an undergrad in Studio Art and Biology at Stanford University. He enjoys oil painting, late-night piano improv and over-thinking things. After graduating, he plans to attend medical school.

SAPPHIRE · JUSTIN TORRES · JACKSON TAYLOR · AYANA MATHIS · CHRIS ADRIAN

THE WRITER'S FOUNDRY MFA

Fall 2013
www.sjcny.edu/mfa

St. Joseph's College
NEW YORK

A Cluster of Stars

SARANAC REVIEW

Issue 8

Finally. A literary journal that bridges the gap
between regional and national and crosses borders:
The Saranac Review.

Featuring quality poetry and prose from Canada and the
United States. An eclectic, diverse array of emerging and
established writers that reflects the expansive, bright spirit of the
etymology of its name, Saranac, meaning "cluster of stars."

research.plattsburgh.edu/saranacreview

Fjords

Edited by John Gosslee

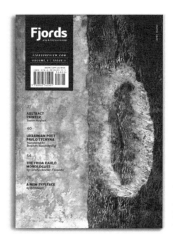

TWICE YEARLY PRINT
ONLINE MONTHLY VERSE
THE LITERARY OBSESSION